D1095319

By the same Author

ROCKET PROPULSION (*Second edition*)

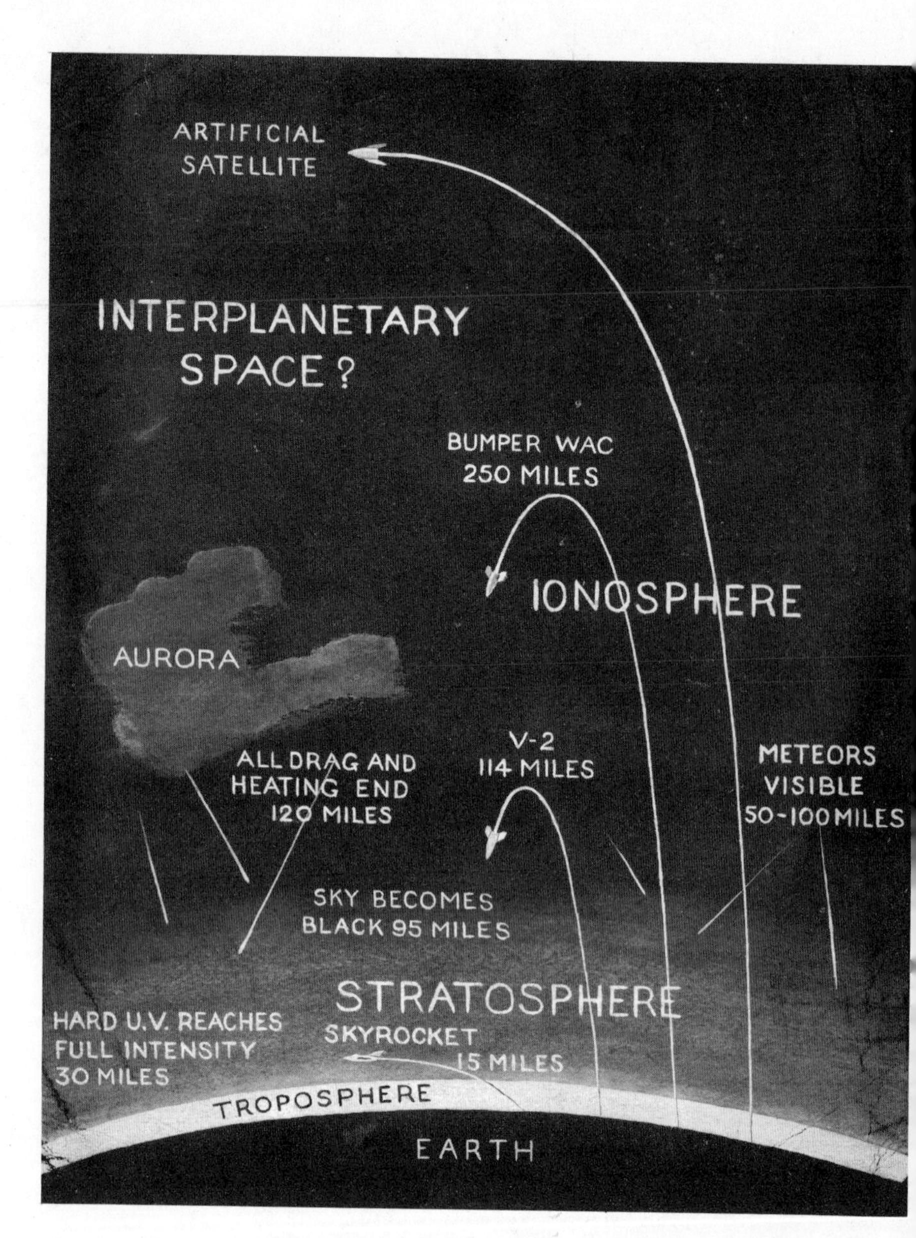

EXPLORING THE FRONTIER TO SPACE

Frontispiece

FRONTIER TO SPACE

by

ERIC BURGESS
F.R.A.S.

With a Foreword
by the Astronomer Royal

SIR HAROLD SPENCER JONES
M.A., Sc.D., F.R.S., F.R.A.S.

THE MACMILLAN COMPANY
NEW YORK

First American Edition, 1956

Library of Congress Catalog card number: 56-9358

PRINTED IN THE UNITED STATES OF AMERICA

FOREWORD

The development of long-range rockets, which had made slow progress in the years before the war, received a great stimulus under the exigencies of war, culminating in the German V-2 rocket. This rocket was a considerable technical achievement, though it is questionable whether its production as a wartime weapon was wise; whether, in fact, the demands on scientific and technical manpower required for its development could not have been better utilized in the production of more conventional weapons.

It is a matter for satisfaction when, out of the waste and destruction caused by war, some dividends, however modest, can be obtained which are of benefit to mankind. The German success in the development of the V-2 has concentrated attention on the potentialities of this new type of weapon. Much development work has been done, particularly in the United States; at the same time, facilities have been freely given to scientists to make use of the opportunities, which high-altitude rockets can provide, of acquiring information that can not be obtained in any other way.

Balloons have been much used in recent years to obtain information about the density, temperature, pressure, humidity and composition of the atmosphere and about the winds at different heights, by the use of radio-sonde and other equipment. Photographic plates have been sent up to high altitude for cosmic-ray and allied investigations, and have recorded particles with energies far exceeding those which can be produced in any of the various large and expensive modern machines used for accelerating particles to very high velocities. But the greatest height reached by balloons is 20 miles, whereas rockets can reach without difficulty heights exceeding 100 miles; the highest altitude so far attained by rocket technique is 242 miles.

By installing suitably designed equipment in the nose-cones of rockets which are shot up to high altitudes, much new knowledge has been gained in many different fields of investigation. The design of instruments that can be fitted into the limited space in the nose-cone, that can withstand the very high acceleration of the rocket after it is projected, and that can either record the required data or telemeter information back to the ground, has required much ingenuity. Because of the high speed of the rocket, the instruments must record their data with negligible lag, while the aerodynamic heating of the rocket when in flight requires precautions to be taken in the design and installation of the instrumentation.

There is a considerable risk that the equipment and records may not be recovered intact after the firing. The expenditure of much time, labour and money may prove of no avail. But this is a risk that must be faced.

Nevertheless in spite of all the difficulties involved, much knowledge has already been gained through the use of rockets: the spectrum of the Sun has been photographed in the far ultra-violet region which, because of absorption by the ozone layer in the atmosphere, is unobservable from the Earth's surface; the existence of currents circulating in the upper atmosphere, which had been conjectured in order to account for geomagnetic variations, has been established: information about the composition, temperature, pressure, density and air movements in the upper atmosphere has been obtained; ionization processes and cosmic-ray phenomena have been studied.

In this book a connected account has for the first time been given of these various fields of investigation, the methcds employed and the results so far obtained. The use of high-altitude rockets for scientific investigation is a tribute to man's ingenuity and resourcefulness. The author has been at great pains to collect together information and data that have hitherto been available only in technical papers and reports. The lists of references to these original sources, which are given at the end of each chapter, will be useful to readers who wish to obtain further information about any of the subjects dealt with. I am sure that all the readers of this book will find, as I have done, this account of pioneer work to be of absorbing interest.

H. SPENCER JONES

PREFACE

THIS is the story of how man has extended his knowledge of the vast regions of the Earth's atmosphere which stretch above the troposphere to the frontier of interplanetary space. With the continued increase in the operating altitude of manned aircraft, the development of guided missiles and long-range rockets, and the talk of manned flight into space, interest concerning these upper regions of the Earth's atmosphere has increased rapidly during the past decade.

During these ten years, too, the newest vehicle for carrying man's instruments into the high atmosphere has been developed, the high-altitude sounding rocket. This has been mainly under the auspices of the United States Government and the various Armed Services, who are to be congratulated on the number of technical papers which they have permitted to be published concerning the results of these researches.

It is hoped that this book will serve as an introduction to the subject, collating most of the modern data and giving to the serious student a useful collection of references to technical papers for further study.

There are a number of references to papers which were presented at the conference on the use of the rocket for high-altitude research which was held at Oxford under the auspices of the Gassiot Committee of the Royal Society in August, 1953. These papers are individually referenced in each chapter, with a general reference to the published proceedings in the bibliography.

The writing of this book would not have been possible without the aid of the data and comments which have been given so freely by various American and other scientists who are working on this fascinating upper-atmosphere research and to whom the writer cannot adequately express his gratitude in the purely formal acknowledgements which follow.

MANCHESTER, ERIC BURGESS
February, 1954

ACKNOWLEDGEMENTS

To the Director and Staff of the United States Naval Research Laboratory for many illustrations, for permission to use material from Upper Atmosphere Reports, for data concerning instrumentations and the results of experiments on solar physics, cosmic rays, rocket orientation, ionospheric characteristics, diffusive separation, ozone layer, atmospheric characteristics, temperature and pressures; and for supplying reprints of published papers on specialized subjects concerning the upper atmosphere.

To the Applied Physics Laboratory of the Johns Hopkins University for details of experiments, for illustrations, the solar ultra-violet spectra and APL spectrograph, and for reprints of APL reports.

To the Air Force Cambridge Research Centre for permission to use data from their reports concerning electron density in the ionosphere.

To the *Journal of Geophysical Research* for permission to reproduce the series of ultra-violet spectra of Fig. 6.17.

To Dr. W. W. Berning of the Ballistics Research Laboratories, Aberdeen Proving Grounds, for permission to quote from his paper concerning the use of DOVAP data for determining charge density in the ionosphere.

To the United States Directorate of Intelligence, Air Force, for photographs and illustrations concerning experiments with the Aeromed Aerobee.

To the Glenn L. Martin Co., and the Aerojet Engineering Corp., for photographs of the Viking rocket and the Aerobee rocket respectively.

To the United States Army Ordnance for photographs of the WAC Corporal and the Bumper-WAC.

To the Director of the Laboratories for Ballistical and Aerodynamical Research, Vernon, for photographs of the Veronique.

To the Pergamon Press Ltd., and the Royal Society, for permission to use illustrations from the papers presented at the Oxford Conference.

To Dr. R. L. Smith Rose, Director of the Radio Research Station, Slough, for supplying the ionosphere sounding record of Fig. 5.1.

To Mullard Ltd. for details and photographs of the Mullard radio *sonde*.

To Mr. F. C. Durant, President of the American Rocket Society, for obtaining photographs which had been previously published in the *Journal of the American Rocket Society*.

To Messrs. C. I. Cummings and A. W. Newberry for supplying photographs of telemetry equipment.

To the Editor of *The Engineer* for the loan of blocks and permission to use material from previously published articles.

To the Editor of *Aeronautics* for permission to use material from previously published articles.

ACKNOWLEDGEMENTS

To Dr. M. O'Day of the Geophysics Research Directorate for photographs of the instrumentation of Aerobee rockets for investigation of day airglow, and for the photograph of the bi-axial Sunseeker.

To Dr. N. W. Spencer of the University of Michigan for permission to use material from Upper Air Research Programme Report No. 2, and for supplying illustrations concerning experiments by the University.

To Dr. S. A. Goudsmit, Editor of *The Physical Review* and to Dr. F. L. Whipple of Harvard College Observatory, for permission to use data from a paper by the Rocket Panel which was originally published in *The Physical Review*.

To The Astronomer Royal for the tracing of the Abinger magnetogram.

To The Editor of *The Astrophysical Journal* for permission to reproduce Fig. 6.11.

To Mr. D. A. Lea for the jacket design.

To my wife for help with the preparation of the book and the proof-reading.

To the staff of Messrs. Chapman & Hall Ltd., whose care and attention made the production of this book possible.

CONTENTS

LIST OF PLATES

(*All other figures are in the text*)

Chapter One

PROBING THE FRONTIER

⩾ ⫴ ⩽

WHEN it arrives at the proving ground from the factory, the forty-five-foot-long cylinder of gleaming aluminium alloy, which is a Viking rocket, seems hardly capable of ascending at a speed of five times faster than sound into the higher regions of the Earth's atmosphere. But that is just what such a rocket can do and, moreover, it is able to carry more than half a ton of scientific instruments with it on its flight.

At White Sands the rocket is first stored in a hangar where it is carefully examined to ensure that no faults have developed during the long rail journey from Maryland, where it was constructed in the Glenn L. Martin factories. Then while it is lying in a horizontal position and mounted over hangar work-stands, which are adjusted in height to facilitate the operations, checking of the wiring, controls, and the rocket-motor valves and propellent controls takes place. Air pressure and power points are available and special test boxes are used to ensure that the gyroscopes, amplifiers, valves and the complex electronics of the missile are all functioning correctly. These exhaustive tests need several days for their completion and only when all has been passed by the engineers and scientists is the rocket moved out to the launching platform.

There it is raised on to the firing table by means of a large mobile servicing gantry which runs on rails and has a number of drawbridge-type platforms from which the scientists and technicians can easily work at the various levels of the tall rocket.

The Viking stands upright on its four tail fins, sitting on blocks mounted on these fins close to their tips. The launching table itself is constructed from welded steel members and it can be tilted slightly in order to direct the rocket up the range or slightly to east or west. This table is bolted down to the main steel structure of the launching platform which bridges a deep pit containing water into which the rocket jet can exhaust, to prevent the raising of clouds of dust by the firing, which would otherwise obscure observation during static tests and at the beginning of a flight. The whole is stressed to withstand the thrust of 20,000 pounds developed by the rocket motor when it is static fired. For this purpose the rocket is held down by a single bolt through each fin block.

Having been set up on its launching table the rocket has then to go through further tests in the vertical position. At this stage the workmen must be protected from the desert climatic conditions and the rocket itself screened from wind-blown sand and, accordingly, a metal 'house' is erected around the tail section. The Viking has four tail fins, but when preparations are being made for the static test, the south fin is removed and replaced by a fin structure to give easy access to the motor bay. The replacement fin structure contains a series of pipes from which carbon-dioxide vapour can be sprayed into the motor compartment after the firing, to extinguish any fire should one break out within the motor component.

Firing operation preparations ensure that all the necessary equipment is moved into the launching area and that the rocket is correctly aligned. It is then about four hours from firing time. The servicing crews start to work and first feed the alcohol fuel into its tank. Then the concentrated hydrogen peroxide for the turbine of the fuel-pumps is loaded; the ignitor is fixed into the combustion chamber, the liquid oxygen pumped into its tank and finally the pressurization gases are made ready. Firing time is now as close as fifteen minutes away.

All personnel retire to the control blockhouse some 1,000 feet from the launching platform. Behind the walls of reinforced concrete, operators at a firing desk can safely observe how the test proceeds. Meters record chamber pressures, operation of the pumps and the motor gimbal controls, and all the complex check circuitry of the high-altitude research vehicle. The firing-control officer can cut the motor at any time should the rocket fail to function properly.

At last the static firing test begins. A switch is thrown and a roaring jet issues from the nozzle of the rocket motor and exhausts through the hole in the launching apron, raising clouds of steam which are blown to one side and drift across the desert and which are illuminated brilliantly if the firing takes place at night. After the test has been satisfactorily completed, the rocket is again carefully inspected to make certain that no flaws have arisen during the period of power. Then, all being found correct, the south fin replacement structure is removed and the fin itself placed in position ready for the free flight.

Meanwhile, while the rocket engineers are busy, the physicists have been preparing their instruments which the Viking is to carry high into the upper atmosphere. An instrumented nose cone has been prepared for the rocket vehicle, a 'warhead' carrying some half-ton or so of scientific apparatus such as cosmic-ray telescopes, ultra-violet solar spectrographs, cloud chambers, photon counters, radio transmitters and pressure- and temperature-sensitive devices. These instruments are accompanied by involved electronic circuits and hundreds of radio valves and it is of utmost importance that all this complex equipment should function perfectly throughout the flight. A single resistor, burning out after take-off or shaking loose from its mounting, could ruin an experiment which has cost many hundreds of pounds and several months of work to prepare.

Carefully the scientists install their precious equipment, fitting the nose cone of stainless steel or aluminium alloy to the front of the slim rocket. They work from the topmost platform of the gantry and when the cone has been bolted into position the instrumentations are yet again checked and counterchecked. By the time the rocket engineers have serviced the Viking for its flight, all other associated agencies must be ready; the scientists must have installed their equipment, blockhouse firing crews must be standing by and range crews, safety crews, recovery parties are all alerted. The radar and optical tracking stations have their instruments ready to follow the flight of the missile to the limits of the Earth's atmosphere.

Thus after months of work, teams of engineers and scientists have co-operated to produce a high-altitude research vehicle which is capable of carrying man's instruments higher than ever before. All is ready. Inside the blockhouse the seconds are counted off and the firing switch thrown. The brilliant exhaust flame spears into the pit beneath the apron. But this time there are no bolts to hold this gleaming pencil to the Earth. Tons of complex apparatus lift easily on the jet of roaring flame, a diamond pattern of shock waves iridescent in the cylinder of rushing exhaust gases. The control cable drops away and the rocket is free, accelerating upwards to pass through the wisps of clouds until it becomes a fast-vanishing speck in the hard blue of the desert sky.

After sixty seconds or so the motor cuts, for all the propellents have then been consumed, but by that time the rocket is travelling at a speed of 3,500 miles per hour and momentum carries it on, up and up, into the fringes of the Earth's atmosphere, to the frontiers of interplanetary space. But although it is invisible to the naked eye, it is not lost to the instruments below. Optical and radar trackers are following it all the time, while oscilloscopes and tape-machines record its messages as data on conditions in near-space are telemetered in controlled radio pulses to the ground stations. The peak of the trajectory may be 100 to 150 miles above the surface of the Earth, but within four or five minutes the rocket will have plunged back into the atmosphere to be broken up and scatter its wreckage over the impact area.

But in those four minutes or so it will have gathered, as we shall see, a tremendous amount of new data which will take many months to evaluate, data which can only be obtained at the space frontier.

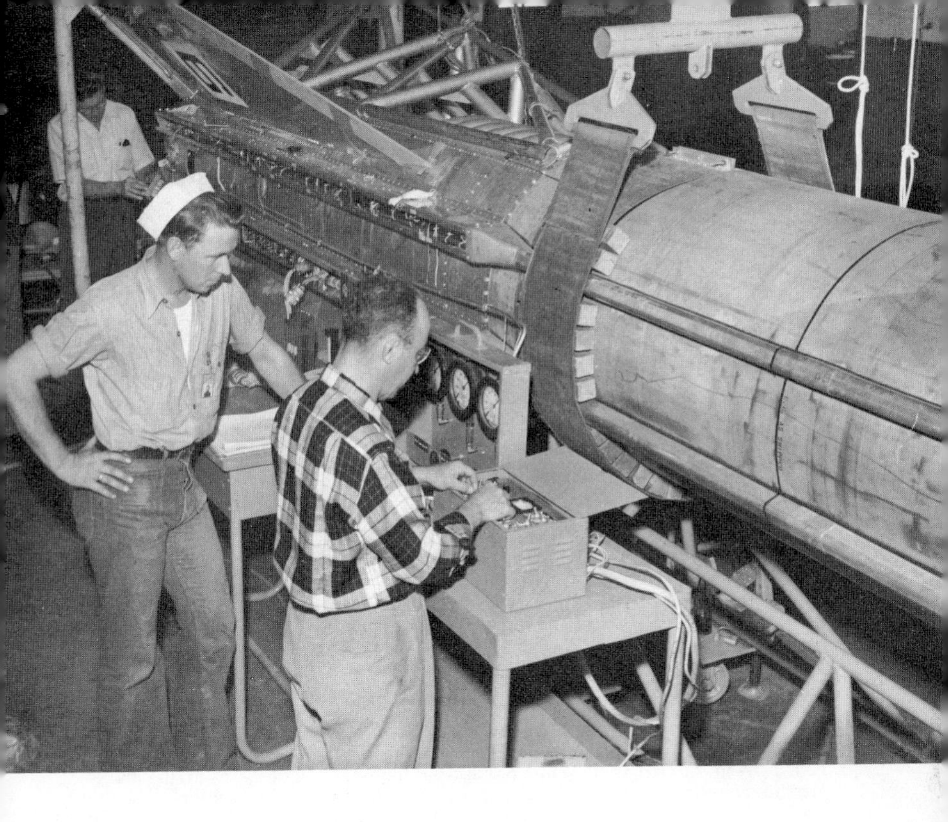

FIG. 1.1—Checking the power plant of the Viking rocket.
(Photo., Glenn L. Martin Co., Courtesy, 'The Engineer')

FIG. 1.2—In the hanger at White Sands with the Organ Mountains in the background, the steam jets, roll and yaw controls for the rocket motor, and the instrument section are checked.

(*Photo., Glenn L. Martin Co., Courtesy, 'The Engineer'*)

FIG. 1.3—To protect workmen from the cold, and the equipment from windblown sand, a metal 'house' is constructed to surround the bottom of the rocket.

(*Photo., Glenn L. Martin Co.*)

FIG. 1.4—During static tests the south fin of the rocket is replaced by this structure in order to provide working access to the intricate equipment inside the motor compartment.

(*Photo., Glenn L. Martin Co.*)

FIG. 1.5—Inside the concrete and steel blockhouse all is ready for the test.

(*Photo., Glenn L. Martin Co.*)

FIG. 1.6—Static firing of the rocket. The Viking is bolted to the launching platform to keep it from taking off. The exhaust jets into a pit filled with water which creates the steam shown on the right.

Photo., Glenn L. Martin Co.)

FIG. 1.7—Equipment in the control compartment of a Viking rocket is checked prior to firing.

(Photo., Glenn L. Martin Co., Courtesy, 'The Engineer')

Chapter Two

THE STORY UNFOLDS

⋗ ≘ ⋖

AN atmosphere is defined as a gaseous envelope surrounding a body in space. The atmospheres of the various planets in the solar system appear to differ very greatly; those of the giant planets such as Jupiter and Saturn seem to consist principally of ammonia and methane and are probably many thousands of miles in depth. The smaller planets like the Earth and Mars have much less dense atmospheres but, nevertheless, even concerning these inner planets we only have a fair amount of data regarding the atmosphere of our own planet; the constituents of the other planetary atmospheres are very much in doubt. Whether or not a planetary body can possess an atmosphere depends upon two governing factors: first the gravitational attraction of the planet, which, together with the planetary radius, determines the escape velocity at points in space surrounding it; and, secondly, the temperature of the outer shell of the atmosphere, which determines the velocity the molecules or atoms of the gases will acquire. If these particles can reach speeds in excess of escape velocity at the fringes of the atmosphere, the gases will gradually leak into space and the world would be, or would become, an airless one. This appears to have happened in the case of the Moon and the planet Mercury and, moreover, it is postulated that light gases such as hydrogen and helium, which are able to reach high molecular velocities, are escaping from the Earth's atmosphere as fast as they are released into it from the surface of the planet.

The lowest region of the atmosphere is known as the troposphere. It is that part of the gaseous envelope in which there is much turbulence and in which clouds are produced by the condensation of water vapour. This was the only region of the air which was known to man when science began to develop at the close of the Middle Ages.

Galileo had noted the difficulty of raising water in pumps, and one of his pupils, Torricelli, associated this difficulty with the pressure of the air. In 1643 he made his announcement of the discovery of air pressure, that is, the weight of the column of air stretching up to the limit of the atmosphere. Torricelli found that the pressure of the atmosphere was sufficient to support a column of mercury about 30 inches (760 mm.) in height, and this was, in fact, equivalent to a pressure of 14·7 pounds per square inch (1·03 kg./sq. cm.). It is usual in upper-atmosphere work to speak of pressures in millimetres of mercury.

The next stage in the extension of man's knowledge of the atmosphere was the determination of a fall in pressure with increasing altitude, thereby confirming that atmospheric pressure does, indeed, result from the weight of the column of air above the recording instrument. This test was made by Pascal who took a barometer (as Torricelli's instrument was called) to the summit of the Puy de Dôme in France and found that the mercury level fell to a value indicative of the increased altitude.[1]

Estimates were next made of the height of the atmosphere. One cannot conclude that because air is about 10,000 times lighter than mercury, the atmosphere is 10,000 times 760 mm. high. This is because the density of the atmosphere falls off rapidly with increasing altitude so that the actual height is very much greater than the five miles (8 km.) or so one would obtain from such a calculation. Edmund Halley made one of the first scientific estimates of the height of the atmosphere. This was in 1714, and he based it on measurements of pressure made by mountain climbers, on Boyle's Law and on the appearance and disappearance of meteor trails, concluding that the atmosphere was about 45 miles (70 km.) high. Furthermore, he showed that its temperature should decrease with increasing height.

Balloonists later confirmed part of Halley's theory by finding that the temperature does, in fact, decrease with increasing altitude at the rate of about 1° C. for each 540 feet (160 metres) of altitude. But balloons went higher and higher and it was soon realized that this law did not hold above certain heights which were found to vary with the latitude.

In 1804 the first balloon ascent of any scientific importance was made by Gay-Lussac and Biot. They reached an altitude of 23,000 feet (7,000 metres) and ascertained that the proportion of water vapour decreased with altitude but that the chemical composition of the atmosphere did not change.

Around mid-century it was found also that the decrease in temperature with altitude was only an average effect. Sometimes meteorological conditions were such that the temperature could increase with altitude, producing what is known as a temperature inversion.

Towards the end of the nineteenth century the idea was put forward of sending up an unmanned balloon with instruments only—

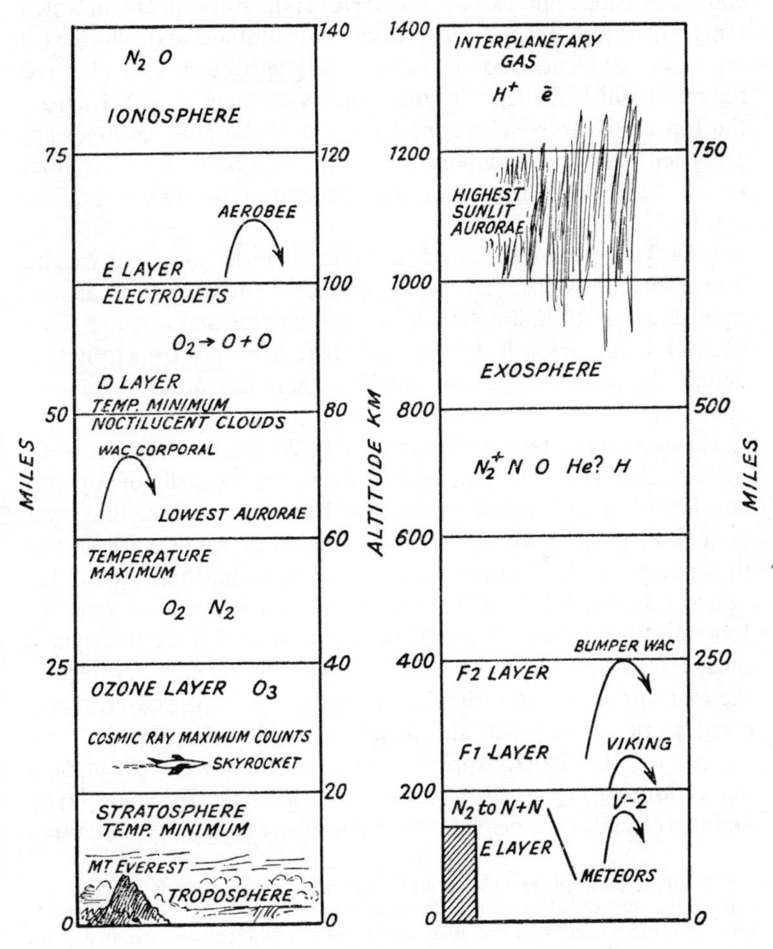

FIG. 2.1—Diagram showing the main regions of the atmosphere.

what is termed a sounding balloon or balloon *sonde*—to heights where unprotected human beings could not survive. Consequently in 1893 Hermite and Besançon sent some instruments to an altitude of 40,000 feet (12,000 metres) and discovered that the lowest temperature recorded was only 222° K.* By the end of the century sounding balloons had reached 72,000 feet (22,000 metres) and obtained valuable new data. From these results a French meteorologist, Teisserenc de Bort, put forward his theory that the atmosphere could be divided into two definite regions; the troposphere, in which the temperature generally decreases with altitude and which is a region of turbulence and of weather, and the stratosphere, a layered region in which the temperature remains constant at 220° K. from the top of the troposphere until the top of the atmosphere is approached. Some contemporary theories suggested, however, that above the stratospheric region the temperature would again fall to extremely low values.

It has now been ascertained that these theories were partly right. The turbulent tropospheric region extends from sea level to an altitude of about 10 miles (16 km.) at the equator and about 5 miles (8 km.) at the poles. But the stratosphere is now known to have a definite limit and, moreover, within it there are winds blowing at high speeds.

The next important discovery was made independently in 1902 by two scientists using radio waves; they were Kennelly of America and Heaviside of England. They postulated the existence of a layer of ionized gases to account for a reflection of wireless waves and thus make possible long-range wireless communication around the bulge of the Earth (Fig. 2.2). This ionized layer became known as the Kennelly-Heaviside layer and it not only showed that the atmosphere must extend up to 60 miles (100 km.) but also added a new region, the ionosphere, to the earlier atmospheric model. Moreover, theoretical work showed that the temperature must be high in these ionized regions. Later, Appleton, of England, discovered an even higher ionized layer which became known as the Appleton layer, and this extended the height of the atmosphere to just over 200 miles

* In upper-atmosphere physics and most scientific work, temperatures are expressed in degrees absolute (°K.). Absolute zero is − 273° C., hence temperatures in degrees centigrade are given by °K. − 273 and temperatures in degrees absolute are ° C. + 273. Accordingly 222° K. is equal to − 51° C.

(320 km.). The ionosphere is thus a great region above the stratosphere in which radiations from the Sun cause the molecules and atoms of the atmospheric gases to become electrically excited. They can become so excited that they lose electrons and become what are known as positive ions. Atoms can be singly ionized, i.e. having lost one electron, doubly ionized (losing two electrons), and multiply-ionized. In exceptional cases, cosmic-ray primaries, for example, they may lose all the electrons and can then become, say, in the case of tin, 50-fold ionized. Sometimes an atom can take-up an electron and become a negative ion.[2] The energy required to produce these

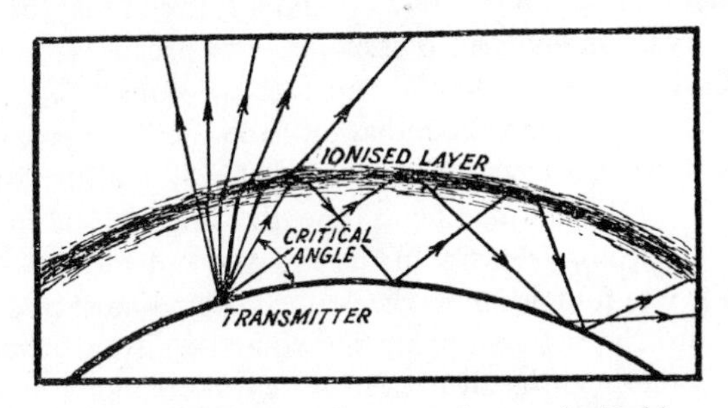

FIG. 2.2—Reflection of radio waves from an ionized layer.

ionized states can be found and it is usually expressed as an ionization potential. For example, the ionization potential of hydrogen is 15·5 volts. Now this represents the potential difference through which an electron must fall to ionize the atom. The energy of an electron which has fallen through one volt can be found to be $1{\cdot}601 \times 10^{-12}$ ergs and this is known as an electron volt. Hence 15·5 e.v. are required to ionize a hydrogen molecule. Cosmic-ray particles have energies greater than millions of electron volts and their energies are conveniently expressed in Bev, where 1 Bev $= 10^{10}$ electron volts.

It was found that if radio waves were sent upwards vertically, often they were reflected and arrived back at the receiving station within a period of about one-thousandth of a second. From knowledge of the speed at which the radio wave is propagated, namely 186,000 miles per second (3×10^{10} cm./sec.), the height of the reflecting layer could be calculated. Moreover, from theory, it is possible to calculate the density of the free electrons within the layer. This is known as the electron density and is defined as the number of electrons per cubic centimetre. This could be determined for the densest part of the layer. By using different frequencies of radiation it became possible to detect ionized layers at different heights as we have seen and this depended largely upon a pulse technique which also permitted the calculation of the electron densities.[3] It was found that the highest layers had the greatest electron densities sometimes amounting to a figure of 10^6 electrons per cubic centimetre. Although the electron density is a maximum in the ionized Appleton layer, the degree of ionization, that is the proportion of molecules and atoms which are ionized, increases constantly with altitude.

These layers are given in Table 2.1 and it is found that the electron densities vary diurnally. This is assumed to be because the ionization is produced by solar radiation. A separate proof that the intensity of ionization depends upon the radiation from the Sun, at least in the lower layers, was obtained during the total eclipse of the Sun which occurred in 1931. During the eclipse the intensity of ionization, measured as electron density in the E layer and the F1 layer, was observed. It was found that as the Moon covered more and more of the Sun's disk, thereby stopping the solar rays from reaching the ionosphere, the intensity of ionization fell, becoming a minimum a few minutes after totality. During a recent eclipse, however, a new F layer was observed to form.[4]

TABLE 2.1 *The Ionosphere*

Altitude miles	km.	*Region*	*Ionization* max. No. of electrons per c.c.	*Characteristics*
Above 45	Above 70	Ionosphere	Increases with height	Strongest in daytime
45	70	D layer	Weak 3×10^2	Daytime layer
70	112	E layer	Moderate 10^5	Daytime layer
140	220	F1 layer	Strong $2{\cdot}5 \times 10^5$	Daytime layer
190	300	F2 layer	More strongly 10^6	Day and night layer

Another layer, the G layer, is thought to exist at 250–450 miles (400–700 km.) but the long period reflection from which its existence is inferred may be due to a multiple reflection between the F1 and F2 layers rather than to the presence of a higher layer. The ionosphere is assumed to start at about the lowest ionized layer in the region of 45 miles (70 km.). The height of the top of the region is not known. Later we shall see that the outer fringe of the atmosphere, thousands of miles up, may be termed the exosphere in which the individual atoms of the atmospheric gases move in orbits around the Earth like miniature satellites. The atmosphere is accordingly provisionally divided into three regions (Table 2.2).

TABLE 2.2 *Regions of the Atmosphere*

Altitude *miles*	*Km*	*Region*	*Characteristics*
S.L. to 5–10	S.L. to 8–16	Troposphere	Turbulence and weather
5–10 to 20	8–16 to 32	Stratosphere	Constant temperature except in equatorial zones, high winds
20 upwards	32 upwards	Upper atmosphere	Ionosphere, ionized gases Exosphere, gases moving in free orbits, high temperatures

Nowadays there are many ways in which the properties of the atmosphere can be studied. They fall into two distinct classes; naturally occurring phenomena and probes. Radio methods are an example of a probing technique, while natural-phenomena methods include observations of the aurorae, the night-sky light, meteors, high clouds and magnetic storms. All these various means of study will be discussed in more detail in subsequent chapters in relation to work with the most recent probe, the rocket. Table 2.3 gives summaries of the methods and the type of data obtained with them.

TABLE 2.3 *Exploring the Atmosphere*

Naturally occurring Phenomena	*Height Range*	*Data Obtained*
Meteors	45–150 km.	Temperature and winds
Clouds, noctilucent	85 km.	Temperature, winds
Night-sky glow	100–500 km.	Constituents
Luminous bands	90–180 km.	Constituents, winds
Aurorae	80–1100 km.	Constituents, temperature
Solar radiation	20– 60 km.	Existence of ozone layer
Terrestrial magnetism changes	80–150 km.	Electrical current system
Barometric Oscillations	50–500 km.	Tides, temperatures
Probes		
Sound waves	35– 60 km.	Temperature, winds
Sounding balloons	0– 32 km.	Constituents, pressure, temperature, humidity, cosmic radiation, ozone layer, density, winds
Radio waves	70–500 km.	Ionization, electron density, magnetic field, temperature, constituents
Light waves	20– 40 km.	Temperature, density
Rockets	0–Interplanetary space	Temperature, composition, density, pressure, ionized layers, currents, winds, cosmic radiation, solar radiation

Of the natural phenomena the aurorae are perhaps the most awe-inspiring, especially when observed in high northern or southern latitudes where they can be seen in their full splendour. They take the form of streamers, arches and patches of luminosity which change in colour and brilliance sometimes appearing like coruscant curtains, while at others as though coloured searchlights were sweeping across filmy clouds high in the sky. The aurorae often commence with the appearance of an arch having its apex at the magnetic meridian. Underneath the arch the sky is comparatively black, and this is known as the dark segment, but stars are visible through it. Then slender streamers of bright light can extend towards the magnetic zenith, while sometimes the sky becomes filled with brilliant scintillating lights shooting up from the horizon. The startling thing about all these brilliant displays is the complete absence of sound, something which can be almost frightening if the phenomenon is observed while alone and far removed from the haunts of one's fellow men.

By photographing the aurorae from different stations simultaneously and then by using the principle of triangulation, it has been possible to determine their altitudes. They are found to exist very much higher than was suggested by de la Rue and Müller[5] at the beginning of the present century, who were of the opinion that the aurorae appeared between 1 and 100 miles (1·5 and 160 km.); latest measurements[6] indicate that they take place between 40 miles (60 km.) and 700 miles (1,100 km.). Most aurorae occur, however, between 55 and 95 miles (90–150 km.) for their lower altitude and 250 miles (400 km.) as the upper height. The highest aurorae, that is those reaching to 700 miles (1,100 km.), are usually sunlit ones. They extend out into the exosphere beyond the shadow cast by the Earth.

The aurorae are now generally accepted as being caused by charged particles which are emitted by the Sun and enter the Earth's upper atmosphere about a day later. The displays have a tendency to repeat with a period equivalent to that of the solar rotation relative to the Earth, that is in 27·6 days and, moreover, they vary in frequency with the 11-year sunspot cycle.

By observing the spectrum of the light emitted by the aurorae some determinations have been made of the composition and temperature of the regions in which they occur. It is found, for example, that both nitrogen and oxygen are present at all levels. From these spectra it has been calculated that the temperature must be about 2,000° K. at 80 miles (120 km.) and at least 8,000° K. at 175 miles (280 km.). But these values would appear to be too high when compared with temperature determinations by other methods and, indeed, recent auroral studies have deduced lower temperatures, even lower than those derived from radio methods.

A less spectacular but equally interesting phenomenon is that of the night airglow. If we analyse the light from the sky on a clear moonless night it is found that this light comes from several sources. There is scattered starlight by both the interplanetary dust and the Earth's own atmosphere and then there is a glow originating in the atmosphere itself.

This is the night airglow[7] and it accounts for two-fifths of the light from the night sky. It is believed to be caused by the recombination of ionized atoms and molecules with the electrons and also the recombination of dissociated molecules; a kind of release of stored energy which has been absorbed by the atmosphere during the daytime, and it is brightest around local midnight. Although spectroscopic determination of the origin of the glow is difficult because of the low intensity of the light, it has been found that atomic oxygen, molecular oxygen, and molecular nitrogen are partly responsible. Many of the bands in the night-sky spectrum may be identified with the Herzberg system of O_2[8]. In addition the metal sodium has been detected. At one time this was the cause of a great deal of wonder concerning why this metal should be present in the upper atmosphere as it is so readily oxidized, but it has been shown[9] that the amount of sodium is extremely minute although it resonates strongly, especially under twilight conditions. Its presence can be accounted for by meteoric or interplanetary dust; the impact of interplanetary dust has even been suggested as possibly helping in the emission process.

At the present time there is considerable doubt concerning the height at which the night airglow originates, some authorities place it lower than the E layer[10] while others believe that it comes from a much higher level, almost towards the top of the ionized layers at 300 miles (500 km.)[11]. Measurements made with rockets fired during the night may help ultimately to clear up this controversy.

Luminous bands have been observed in the night sky, as though the airglow were very patchy. Their heights have not been accurately determined and Hoffmeister[12] has suggested that they may be caused by the impact of interplanetary dust.

We have seen that high temperatures are called for in the upper regions of the atmosphere but the change from stratospheric temperature to upper-atmosphere temperatures is not simple. Even in the stratosphere it has been found that the temperature is not constant in the tropics but that it increases with height.

When gunfire became a major feature of warfare a curious effect was noticed in regard to the audibility of the sounds. It was found, for example, that when gunfire was intense, the noise of battle might be heard by people a long way away while those closer to the battle area heard nothing. Similarly when intense volcanic explosions took place, like that at Krakatoa, the same effect was noted. Later, scientists made some controlled attempts to use this anomalous propagation of sound for the study of the upper atmosphere and in 1901 when the firing of 'minute guns' took place on the occasion of Queen Victoria's funeral, the concentric rings of audibility and silence were recorded.

Two explanations for the anomalous propagation were possible. The bending back of the sound waves could be caused by a change in the composition of the atmosphere, the relatively heavy oxygen and nitrogen being replaced by lighter gases such as helium or hydrogen. This was not regarded as a likely explanation because these two gases do not make their presence known in the spectra of the aurorae and the airglow. The other alternative was that a high-temperature layer existed which would act as a reflector of sound waves in the same way that temperature inversions in the troposphere can give rise to optical mirages by the turning of light waves back to Earth. From observations of big bangs which took place at various times, the most important being the planned Heligoland explosion in 1947, it has been deduced that there must be a high-temperature layer at a height of 20 to 40 miles (32 to 64 km.) and within it the maximum temperature is calculated to be 350° K. at an altitude of 31 miles (50 km.). This has been confirmed by the observations of exploding meteors which are found to be rarely audible if they explode above 35 miles (60 km.) for then the sound waves are returned upwards by the warm layer beneath the explosion point.

Also appearing in the upper atmosphere are very high clouds, which are only visible when the Sun is below the horizon at ground level but is still illuminating the regions in which the clouds are formed. Hence they are called noctilucent clouds. Triangulation calculations have shown that these clouds are at an altitude of 50–55 miles (80–90 km.). It is postulated that they may be of ice

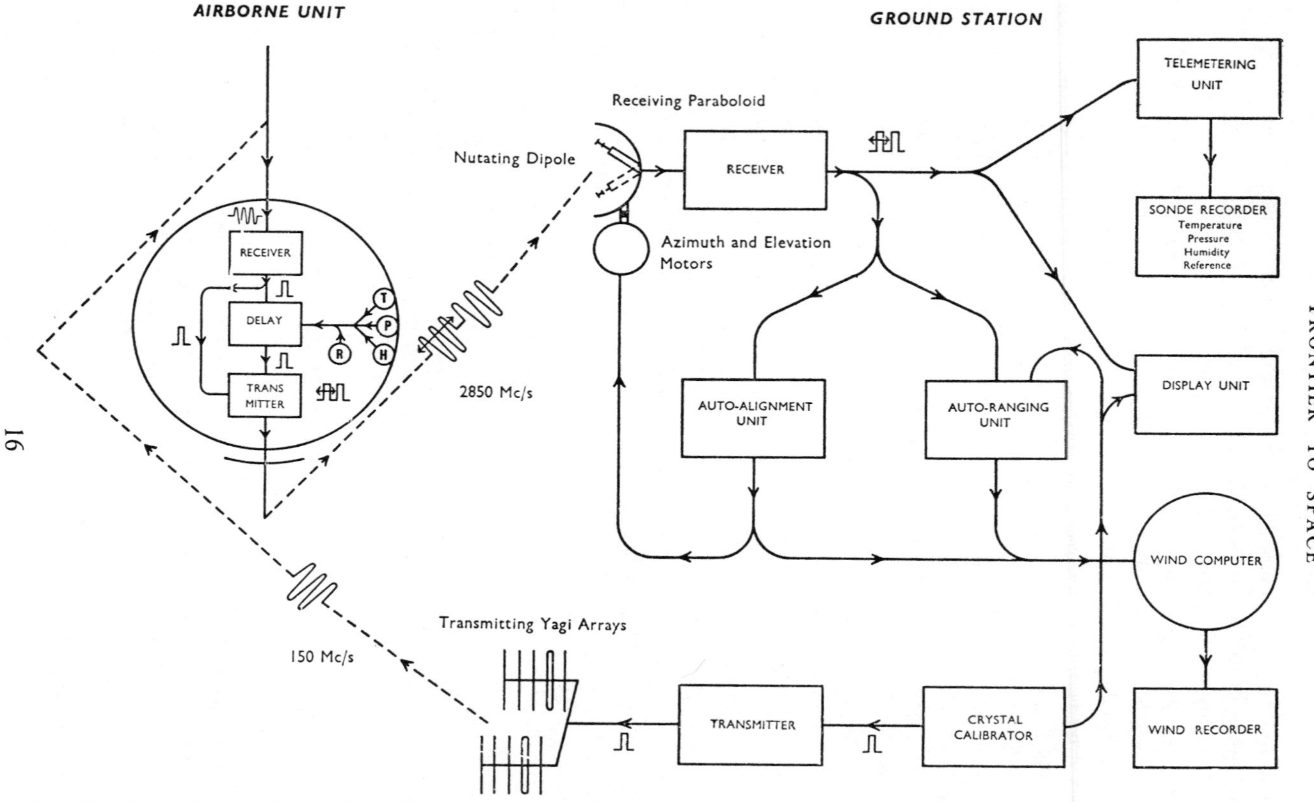

FIG. 2.3—Layout of a radio *sonde* station. The airborne unit, the source of meteorological information is shown on the left-hand side, and the display and recording units on the extreme right. (*Courtesy, Mullard Ltd.*)

crystals, and if that is so there must be a temperature minimum at the height where they occur. We shall see later that this temperature minimum does indeed exist. Another theory assumes that the clouds consist of volcanic dust and similarly, for them to appear in such a narrow layer, this theory also demands that there should be a region of rising temperature above the height at which they are observed.

The investigation and routine examination of the lower atmosphere is carried out mainly by balloon *sondes*. Nowadays the balloon *sonde* is an instrument which gives reliable and accurate data concerning the atmosphere up to about 20 miles (30 km.). Essentially the system of measurement has been divided into two sections; the first deals with atmospheric winds which are determined by optical or radar tracking of a hydrogen filled balloon, which is sometimes known as a Rawind system, while the second is concerned with recording of pressure, temperature and humidity. The radar and optical methods of wind determination, as normally employed, have severe limitations because of drift at high wind speeds. If the equipment is not to be made too heavy for economic use, the balloon drifts out of transmitter range at about 50 miles (80 km.), before it can reach its ceiling.

Pressure, temperature and humidity are determined by a radio *sonde* in which the readings of the measuring instruments are telemetered to the ground station. In recent years the practice has been to put a radar reflector on a radio *sonde* balloon and use one flight for obtaining both types of data.

The most modern system, developed by Mullard,[13] makes possible a considerable extension of range by using a combined radar transponder and *sonde* so that the radar tracking can take place to slant ranges of 115 miles (185 km.), thus making the *sonde* capable of giving data to altitudes of at least 19 miles (30·5 km.). The layout of the radar *sonde* system is shown in Fig. 2.3. The balloon unit is continuously interrogated from the ground station using a frequency of 152·2 Mc/s. and responds at 2,850 Mc/s. The time taken for the response to reach the ground station gives the balloon's range, and the rate of change of this together with the bearing and elevation information gives the wind speed. The direction of the balloon is obtained from a rotable aerial system using a receiving paraboloid with a nutating dipole like that used in anti-aircraft fire control radar. The transmitting Yagi aerials are actually mounted on the same paraboloid mount (Fig. 2.4).

A second pulse from the balloon unit also at 2,850 Mc/s, transmits by means of a variable delay the data on temperature, pressure, and humidity, together with a calibration signal. All this information is displayed on recording units at the ground station, by means of

FIG. 2.4—Aerial system for a radio *sonde* ground station. The transmitter radiates through a pair of Yagi aerials while the microwave signals from the balloon transmitter are received by the five feet diameter paraboloid and nutating dipole. The aerial automatically follows the balloon.
(*Photo., Mullard Ltd.*)

cathode-ray oscilloscopes, pen recorders, and teleprinter digital records.

Higher regions have been sounded by radio probes (see Chapter Five) and also by pulsed searchlight beams. Recent work in this connexion has been undertaken under United States Air Force contracts and data concerning temperature and other conditions obtained.[14]

In the past few years the study of the upper atmosphere has become more and more important. Currently rocket-propelled planes are reaching an altitude of 15 miles (24 km.) and are expected to ascend much higher in the coming years. Even commercial airliners such as the Comet have been operating well within the normal stratosphere at 8 miles (13 km.) altitude and development will undoubtedly bring higher-flying airliners as time passes. But of even greater importance has been the need for adequate defence against atomic-bomb attacks which may arise in any future conflict and which has made military people concentrate on the development of target-seeking guided missiles.[15] These have needed an understanding of the operation of vehicles at high speeds and high altitudes. But perhaps the greatest incentive to upper-atmosphere study has been the potentialities of the long-range rocket for strategic atomic bombing[16] and the need for some kind of defence against such weapons. The control of these missiles at velocities of several thousands of miles an hour and the direction at specific targets insist that their operators should know accurately the conditions in the upper atmosphere through which such vehicles must pass. For extreme ranges it may be necessary to use wing surfaces[17] or even richochet effects[18] and accurate data on composition, temperature, and density at extreme heights becomes imperative. And, of course, there are possibilities of flight into space by means of rocket vehicles[19] in which it would be most advantageous to conserve propellents by employing atmospheric braking techniques on the return into the Earth's atmosphere.[20] Indeed, before man can hope to achieve space flight he must understand the Earth's atmosphere and its peculiarities much better than he does at the moment. Moreover, he must test how removal from the atmosphere will affect his living processes; for example, what will be the effects of the intense solar radiations on both himself and his machines, how will the cosmic-ray primary particles come into the picture, and what will be the effects of meteors and interplanetary dust?

Another aspect of the space-flight programme will most likely be the use of a sub-orbital refuelling technique from an orbit around the Earth. Accurate knowledge of the effective height of the Earth's atmosphere is necessary in order to ensure that the orbit of the refuelling operation will be a stable one.

Man is reaching out into space at this time and his machines are even now helping to fill in the many blanks in the picture of the Earth's atmosphere. But it is fascinating how as man learns more and more he finds that there appears to be a limitless extent of unknowns stretching before him. He has gone a long way from Halley's simple conception of the air envelope surrounding the Earth, but modern work indicates that there are endless paths yet to tread.

One thing has to be realized about the Earth's gaseous envelope before proceeding to a discussion of its properties in more detail; this is that the atmosphere is mainly opaque. To the naked eye, neglecting clouds, the air may appear to be a very transparent substance allowing us to see out and observe the other bodies in space

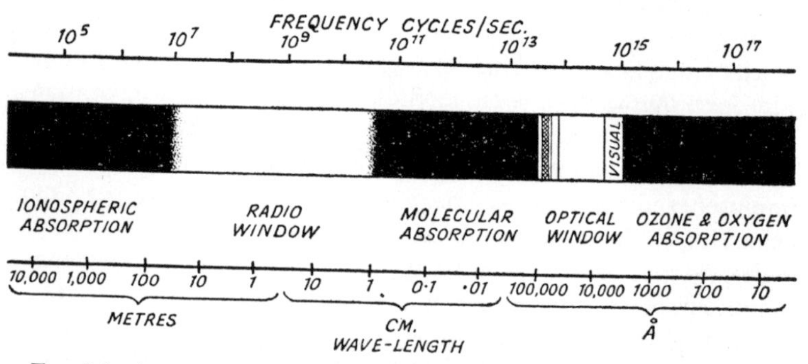

FIG. 2.5—Atmosphere windows. This diagram shows the complete electromagnetic spectrum from the far ultra-violet into radio frequencies. On it are indicated the optical window and the radio window through which radiation of appropriate wavelengths can reach the surface of the Earth. All other radiation is stopped at some level within the atmosphere.

quite clearly. It must be remembered, however, that our eyes observe only a limited range of frequencies of the complete spectrum of electromagnetic radiation. They have, indeed, developed over the many centuries of evolution to respond most strongly to those frequencies of the solar radiation to which the atmosphere is most transparent. Put man on a planet with a different atmosphere and his eyes could be quite inefficient. The human eye responds to light between the wavelengths of about 7,500–4,000 Angstrom units* and the Earth's atmosphere cuts off the light from the Sun in the short wavelength end (the ultra-violet) at about 2,900A. In the infra-red region, absorptions by the atmosphere again cut off the solar

* The Angstrom unit, A, is a length of 10^{-8} cm.

spectrum at about 30,000A., first with what are known as telluric lines and then by molecular absorptions. The atmosphere then remains opaque until the region of wavelengths between just under 1 cm. and 35–45 metres is reached, that is, radio frequencies from about 50,000 Mc/s to 7 or 8 M/cs. The first window in the atmosphere is known as the optical window; the second, the radio window (Fig. 2.5). Until quite recently all observations of the universe had been made through the optical window by telescopes, spectroscopes and cameras receiving and recording light waves in the visible and near-visible regions of the spectrum. During the past decade, however, use has been made of the radio window and radio telescopes have been adding considerably to the science of astronomy.[21]

At the top of the atmosphere, therefore, there is a constant barrage of electromagnetic radiation, principally coming from the Sun but also from other emitting sources in the Universe, the stars, the distant nebulae, the interstellar and interplanetary dust, and by reflected light from the dust and from planetary bodies. In addition, particles impinge on the atmosphere, ranging in size from cosmic radiation primaries, through interplanetary dust, to pieces of material weighing many tons like the great meteorite which fell in Siberia in 1908. Most particles do not penetrate the atmosphere, only the greatest meteors are successful in penetrating to ground level. Smaller meteors are destroyed high in the atmosphere in the 32–80 miles (50 km. to 130 km.) region. Micrometeorites, or interplanetary dust, may be lost even higher, though ultimately it is believed that quantities of this may drift to the surface and add to the mud and silt on the bottom of the oceans. Attempts have indeed been made to measure the quantities of interplanetary and meteoric dust which have fallen during geological time by examining such silt.

Corpuscles are emitted by the Sun and are stopped by the upper atmosphere. These may consist of electrons and protons, and they are thought to give rise to the aurorae and to magnetic storms and ionospheric disturbances of certain types. None of these particles reach sea level.

Higher-energy particles consist of the cosmic-ray primaries. Some are deflected by the Earth's magnetic field, while others manage to penetrate the atmosphere. Few, if any, of the primaries reach sea level. They end their careers either by catastrophic collisions with atomic nuclei or by nuclear transformations into other particles.

The character of the primaries was not really understood until high-altitude rockets had carried cosmic-ray telescopes to altitudes above those at which the destructive action of the atmosphere hid the true nature of the cosmic rays.

Consequently, in order for man to know more of the pure sciences concerned with solar physics, the origin of cosmic radiation and the mechanism of the Universe itself, his instruments must be carried above the thick atmospheric blanket which so restricts his observations and experiments. High-altitude research is accordingly of interest for the development of pure science, the search after truth, as well as the mundane engineering problems concerning the control of long-range missiles designed to obliterate some unsuspecting city in a nuclear holocaust.

We can indeed, as will later be shown, regard the Earth's atmosphere as a vast laboratory. In it, cosmic rays produce nuclear transformations and reactions, solar radiations ionize and dissociate the atmospheric gases, photo-chemical reactions take place between the atmospheric constituents while electromagnetic effects due to solar activity produce currents in the ionized layers, and the propagation of radio and sound waves can be studied and assist in the firmer understanding of radio communication and acoustics.

The study of the atmosphere covers sections of two main spheres of human knowledge; astrophysics, which includes the behaviour of particles and radiations coming from space, and geophysics, encompassing the effects of the atmospheric peculiarities on the Earth itself.

REFERENCES

[1] ELLIS, W., *Quart. Jnl. Roy. Met. Soc.*, **12**, 131, 1886
[2] MASSEY, H. S. W., *Negative Ions*, Cambridge Monographs, 1938
[3] BREIT, G., TUVE, M. A., *Physical Review*, **28**, 554, 1926
[4] SINGER, S. F., *Nature*, **171**, 146, 1953
[5] DE LA RUE, W., MÜLLER, H. W., *Proc. Royal Society*, **30**, 332, 1880
[6] HARANGE, L., *The Aurorae*, Chapman & Hall, 1951
[7] ROACH, F. E., PETTIT, H. B., *Jnl. Geophys. Res.*, **56**, 325, 1951
[8] PILLOW, M. E., *Proc. Physical Society*, A, **66**, 730, 1953
[9] BATES, D. R. *Monthly Notices, Roy. Astron. Soc.*, **109**, 223, 1949
[10] ROACH, F. E., PETTIT, H. B., WILLIAMS, *Jnl. Geophys. Res.*, **55**, 183, 1950
[11] ELVEY, C. T., FARNSWORTH, A. H., *Astrophysical Journal*, **96**, 451, 1942
[12] HOFFMEISTER, C., *Jnl. Brit. Astron. Assoc.*, **62**, 288, 1952
[13] JONES, F. E., HOOPER, J. E. N., ALDER, N. L., *Proc. Inst. Elect. Eng.*, **98** Part II, 461, 1951
[14] FRIEDLAND, S. S., *et al.*, (A) *Physical Review*, **92**, 1080, 1953

[15] WEYL, A. R., *Guided Missiles*, Temple Press, 1949
GATLAND, K. W., *Development of the Guided Missile*, Iliffe, 1954
[16] BURGESS, E., *Rocket Propulsion*, Chapman & Hall, 1954, Ch. VI.
[17] PERRING, W. G. A., *Jnl. Roy. Aeron. Soc.*, **50**, 483, 1946
[18] SANGER, E., BREDT, I., *Raketenflugtechnik*, Vol. II, 1944
[19] MALINA, F. J., SUMMERFIELD, M., *Jnl. Aeron. Sc.*, **14**, 471, 1947
[20] NONWEILER, T. R. F., *Jnl. Brit. Interpl. Soc.*, **10**, 26, 1951, **10**, 258, 1951
[21] LOVELL, B., CLEGG, J. A., *Radio Astronomy*, Chapman & Hall, 1952

Chapter Three

ROCKETS TAKE OVER

⩾ ◦|◦ ⩽

ALTHOUGH unmanned sounding balloons had reached altitudes of 20 miles (32 km.), the highest manned flight was by Stevens and Anderson in the *Explorer II* who ascended to 13·7 miles (22 km.) on 11th November, 1935. During recent years, polyethylene and neoprene sounding balloons, launched in the United States and other countries, have reached altitudes in the region of 25 miles (40 km.) which appears to be the maximum likely to be attained with this method of high-altitude probe. But the rocket, which can develop a thrust in a vacuum and is, in fact, more efficient when its gases are discharging into space, can carry's man's instruments much higher than this. The use of the rocket for altitude sounding is by no means a new idea and has been suggested in the past by Goddard,[1] Oberth,[2] Ley,[3] the GALCIT workers[4] and others.

The first practical sounding rocket was, however, produced by GALCIT. The project commenced in 1936 and finally led to the production of the WAC Corporal rocket which was flight tested during the autumn of 1945. The project had as its initial objective the carrying of 25 pounds (11·5 kg.) of instruments to the sounding-balloon ceiling of at least 19 miles (30 km.), in accordance with the requirements of the U.S. Signal Corps. Some preliminary tests were made at Goldstone Range, California, on 3rd–5th July, 1945, with a one-fifth scale model which was known as the Baby WAC, and from these tests it was concluded that it would be practical to use booster launching and have arrow stability of the rocket by means of three tail fins.

The WAC Corporal rocket was 16 feet (4·8 metres) long and had a diameter of 12 inches (30 cm.). It was cylindrical in shape with a conical nose fairing. The dry weight was 300 pounds (136 kg.) and the take-off weight, 665 pounds (301 kg.) when loaded with the propellents

FIG. 3.1—Launching the first high-altitude sounding rocket, the WAC Corporal in 1945—the booster is still attached.
(Photo., U.S. Army)

FIG. 3.2—The control blockhouse at White Sands Proving Grounds showing a Viking rocket in the servicing gantry in the background. The launching is controlled from this blockhouse and observations made from its safety.
(Photo., Glenn L. Martin Co.)

[*Between pp. 24–25*

FIG. 3.4—The Aerobee rocket with booster attached being moved on a trailer for placing in the launching tower shown on the right of the picture.

(*Photo., Aerojet Engineering Corporation*)

FIG. 3.6—The first two-step rocket, the Bumper WAC takes off from White Sands to ascend 242 miles into the ionosphere.

(*Photo., U.S. Army Ordnance*)

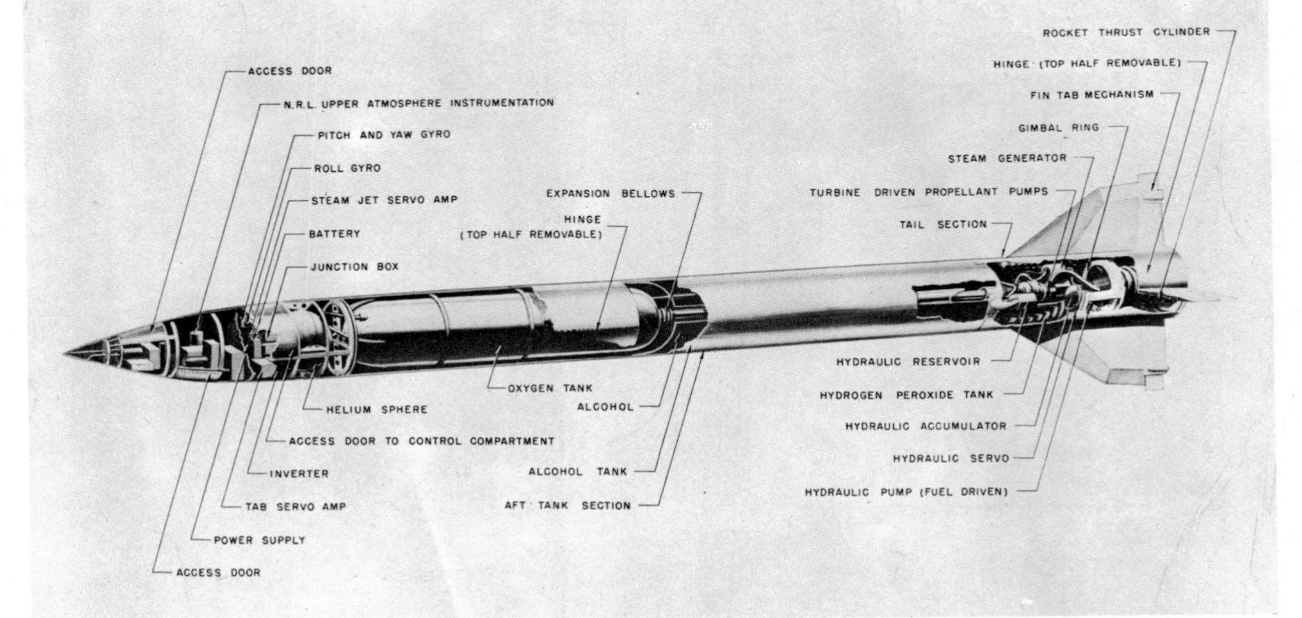

FIG. 3.5—Cutaway drawing of the Viking rocket showing the location of the compoment parts, the controls and the instrumentation.

Courtesy, Glenn L. Martin Co.)

FIG. 3.9—Viking No. 4 rises on its way to the upper atmosphere on 11th May 1950, from the equator, south of Hawaii. It reached an altitude of 106·4 miles.

(*Photo., Glenn L. Martin Co.*)

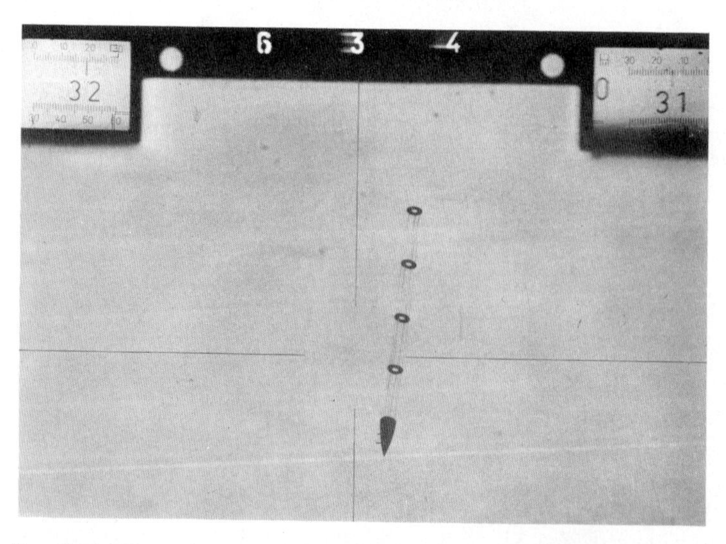

FIG. 3.10—Illustrating a method of recovery for the instrumented nose cone. Here the Veronique nose cone is falling slowly under the influence of drag discs.

(*Photo., Service E. A. Propulsion*

of nitric acid (oxidizer) and aniline (fuel). The rocket motor was regeneratively cooled by circulating the fuel through a cooling space between the double walls of the combustion chamber and nozzle, while the propellents were displaced from their tanks to the combustion chamber by air pressure. A thrust of 1,500 pounds (680 kg.) was maintained for a period of 45 seconds. The motor was developed by the Aerojet Engineering Corporation.

In order to attain high altitudes, a solid propellent booster rocket started the WAC Corporal on its upwards flight. The booster was a modified version of the Navy TINY TIM air-to-sea missile and it developed a thrust of 50,000 pounds (23,000 kg.) for a period of 0·5 seconds. The booster had not quite finished firing when the rocket reached the top of the 102 feet (31 metres) high, three-rail launching tower. The rails of this tower were 120 degrees apart and had an effective length of 80 feet (24·5 metres).

Firing tests of the WAC Corporal were carried out at White Sands Proving Grounds, Las Cruces, New Mexico, (geomagnetic latitude, 41° N.) between 26th September, 1945, and 25th October, 1945 (Fig. 3.1). These proving grounds have seen the launching of most of the world's high-altitude rockets. The area of the proving grounds extends for about 125 miles (200 km.) in a north–south direction and has a maximum width, at the north end, of just over 40 miles (65 km.). The rocket range consists mainly of a desert plateau, having an elevation of about 4,000 feet (1,200 metres) above sea-level and lying between the San Andres Mountains and the Sacramento Mountains which have peaks rising to 10,000 feet (3,000 metres). The main feature of the range, other than the launching tower and a servicing gantry, is the control blockhouse (Fig. 3.2), which is the nerve centre of the rocket launching and control system. It is situated about 1,000 feet (300 metres) away from the launching point and consists of a squat structure with walls of concrete ten feet (3·05 metres) thick, surmounted by a pyramidal roof of reinforced concrete which is 27 feet (8·23 metres) thick at the apex.

After the firing of the WAC Corporal, its course was tracked by three radar stations and five special camera units, installed for this purpose and operated by personnel of the Aberdeen Ballistics Research Laboratory. Moreover, the missile itself sent information back to the ground while it was in flight by using radio telemetering. The original telemetering system operated by making each quantity which had to be measured vary the frequency of an audio oscillator. Five such variable audio-frequencies were used to modulate a radio frequency (100 Mc/s) carrier. At the ground station, suitable filter circuits enabled the five audio-frequency data modulations to be selected for recording. In fact, two such installations were used in the one rocket, thus giving a ten-channel telemetering system.

It so happened that the WAC Corporal was not destined to be used extensively for upper-atmosphere research because at the time when its development was completed, the war in Europe ended and a large number of captured German V-2 rockets became available. Parts for these were originally shipped to the United States so that the missiles could be assembled and fired in order to give military personnel experience of the handling of large rockets. The Army Ordnance planned to use twenty-five V-2 rockets which were to be assembled and fired by the General Electric Company. Firings were to take place from the White Sands Proving Grounds.

However, at the close of 1945, it was suggested that upper-atmosphere research might be done with these rockets and accordingly several universities and research agencies were invited to propose experiments and instrumentations which could profitably be flown. The V-2 Upper Atmosphere Panel was formed early in 1946 and the first American-launched V-2 ascended from White Sands on 16th April, 1946[5] (Fig. 3.3).

Complete details of the V-2 rocket have been given in the literature, especially by Perring[6] and Kooy and Uytenbogaart[7]. Essentially this missile was a large liquid propellent rocket using ethyl alcohol as fuel and liquid oxygen as oxidizer. These liquids were pumped into a combustion chamber, the fuel being used as a coolant. The motor developed a thrust of 60,000 pounds (27,000 kg.) for a period of about 70 seconds. Dry weight of the rocket amounted to 8,690 pounds (3,950 kg.) and it carried 19,310 pounds (8,750 kg.) of propellents. The overall length of the rocket was 46 feet (14 metres) and the maximum body diameter 5 feet 5 inches (1·65 metres). The warhead weighed 2,150 pounds (980 kg.) and this became the available payload weight. At the time when the burning of the propellents was completed, the rocket reached its maximum speed of about 3,500 miles per hour (5,600 km./hr.). In later firings from White Sands, the payload was increased by nearly 50 per cent with complete success.

After the original flight series the Army later altered its programme

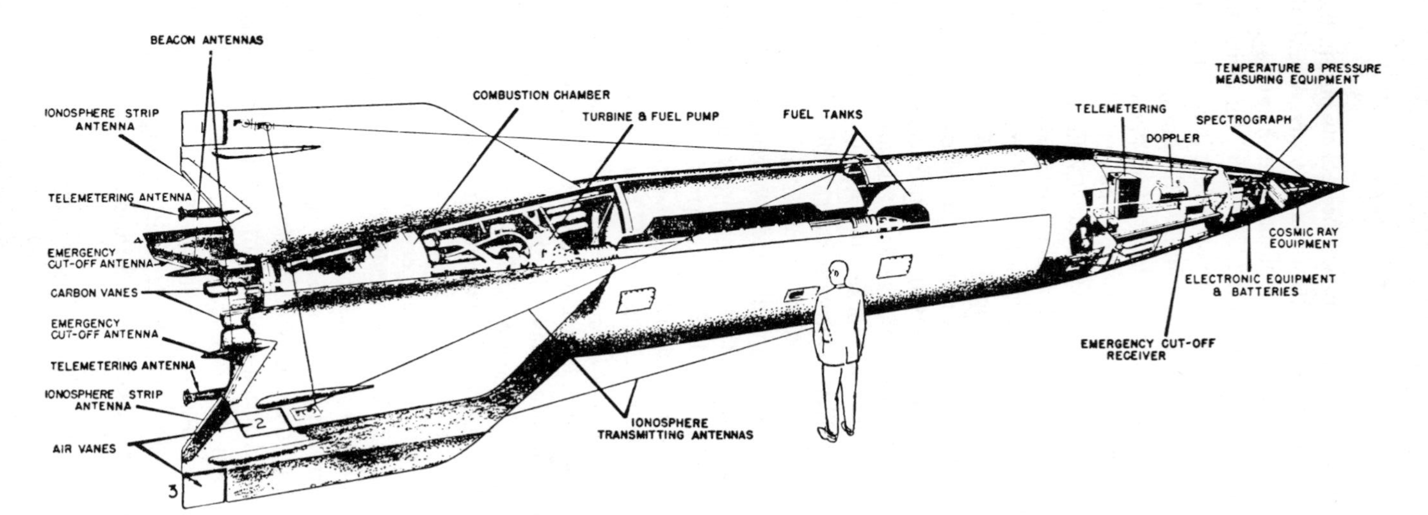

FIG. 3.3—A V-2 rocket instrumented for upper atmosphere study showing the location of instruments in the warhead and control chamber and the various aerial systems.
(*Courtesy*, *Naval Research Laboratory*)

to plan for the firing of seventy-five of the rockets but, in fact, the total fired came to sixty-six over a period of six years. A peak altitude of 133 miles (214 km.) has been established and the average altitude reached by the rockets was 60 miles (95 km.). If, for estimating the average height, complete failures are excluded, it is found that the average peak height was just over 80 miles (128 km.).

It was realized quite soon in the upper-atmosphere research programme that other rockets would have to replace the V-2s when they were either used up in flights or deteriorated with storage. Accordingly, as early as May 1946 the Bureau of Ordnance awarded a contract for the design and construction of twenty smaller high-altitude rockets which were to be developed from the WAC Corporal but which would have a peak altitude of about twice that of the earlier American rocket. The motor was again constructed by the Aerojet Engineering Corporation and the rocket structure by the Douglas Aircraft Company. This new rocket, the Aerobee,[8] emerged as a vehicle similar to the WAC Corporal but slightly larger. It was, in one version, just under 19 feet (5·78 metres) in length and had a diameter of 15 inches (38 cm.). Fully loaded it weighed 1,100 pounds (500 kg.) and was intended to carry a payload of 160 pounds (73 kg.) to an altitude of 85 miles (135 km.). Arrow stability was again achieved by means of three tail fins (Fig. 3.4).

A solid-propellent booster, weighing 547 pounds (248 kg.), having a large thrust and operating for just under two seconds, was used to accelerate the missile up a launching tower which was 140 feet (43 metres) in height and which had rails 95 feet (29 metres) in length. The booster was electrically fired and gave the Aerobee a speed of 700 miles per hour (1,100 km./hr.) when a pressure regulator started the liquid-propellent motor. This fired for 45 seconds producing a final velocity of about 2,700 miles per hour (4,300 km./hr.) at an altitude of 18 miles (29 km.). Five cubic feet (0·142 cu. metres) of space were provided for instrumentation.

The first live Aerobee was launched on the 24th November, 1947, reaching a peak altitude of 37 miles (60 km.). This was below theoretical maximum because the motor had to be cut due to an abnormal trajectory. The second Aerobee, fired 3rd May, 1948, reached an estimated peak of 71 miles (114 km.) and since that date the rocket has proved a most reliable vehicle giving, in recent years, one hundred per cent calculated performance.

But in addition to the Aerobee there is a need for a larger rocket which can ascend to the higher regions of the atmosphere and which can carry payloads comparable to the V-2 to heights above 100 miles (160 km.). Glenn L. Martin, in conjunction with Reaction Motors, and under the supervision of the Naval Research Laboratory, produced this rocket. Originally it was to be called the Neptune, but finally it was named the Viking in order to prevent confusion with the Neptune aircraft. This high-altitude vehicle is, at the time of going to press, still in the development stage and its dimensions vary from missile to missile. Early versions were about the same length as the V-2 rocket but had only about half its diameter. The gross weight of the rocket was about 7·5 tons of which, by use of light alloy materials for construction wherever possible, 80 per cent consisted of propellents. Accordingly the Viking is a high-performance rocket so that, despite its smaller size and lower thrust motor, it can carry payloads similar to those of the V-2 to equivalent heights (Fig. 3.5).

The operation and performance of rocket vehicles have now extensive references in the literature.[7, 9, 10, 11, 12] The peak altitude of a sounding rocket is proportional to the square of the specific impulse and it increases exponentially with the mass ratio. The specific impulse has the dimension of time, it is the jet exhaust velocity divided by the acceleration of gravity. It depends upon the propellents used and the thermal efficiency of the motor, being increased by high-combustion-chamber temperatures and pressures and low molecular weight in the exhaust gases. The mass ratio is the ratio between the take-off weight and the dry weight of the rocket. For the V-2 it was 3·7, the Aerobee 2·2 and the Viking 4·0. Larger rockets can attain higher altitudes than small ones because the drag force does not increase proportionately with size, while at the same time the possible mass ratio increases with size.

By jettisoning propellent tanks during flight, a system which is known as expendable construction,[13] or by using a step principle[14] whereby rockets are placed one within the other, succeeding rockets being fired as soon as the previous one ends its burning period, greater altitudes can be obtained. An excellent example of the step principle is given by the Bumper-WAC,[15] a combination of V-2 and WAC Corporal (Fig. 3.6). The smaller American rocket was mounted at the nose of the V-2 and fired when the V-2 had used all its propellents. Separation of the two rockets took place at an altitude of about 25 miles (40 km.) as the V-2 attained its peak velocity. The small WAC Corporal then burned its own propellents and boosted its speed to about 5,100 miles per hour (8,200 km./hr.) thus reaching a peak altitude of 242 miles (390 km.) on 24th February, 1949. This is the greatest altitude reached by man's instruments as far as the author is aware.

Acceleration of the V-2 ranged from 1·64g effective at take-off, to about 6g at all-burnt (Fig. 3.7). Instrument design was not, therefore, seriously hindered by excess inertial forces. The same applies to the Viking rocket, but in the case of the Aerobee, allowance has to be

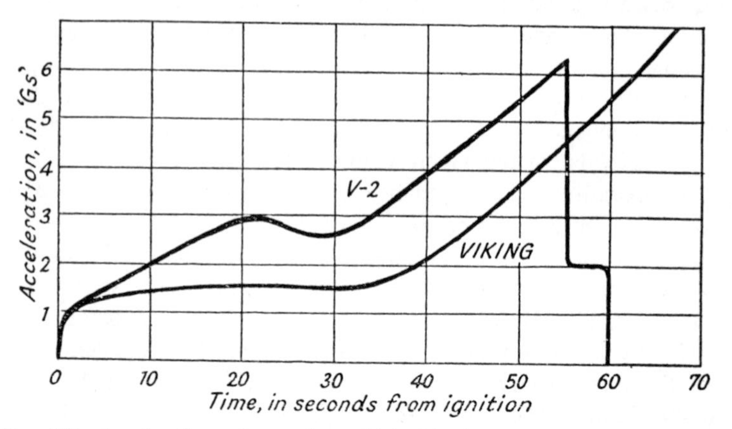

FIG. 3.7—Acceleration of two large high-altitude rockets, the V-2 and the Viking. These curves show how the greatest accelerations are experienced towards the end of the burning period.

made for the high initial acceleration of 14g which is produced by the solid-propellent booster. Vibration is a major problem in all rockets, especially if the instrumentation is situated at the rear, close to the rocket motor. Most components are now shake-tested before installation by means of a machine which resembles a large loudspeaker. Equipment must, however, be compatible; for example, powerful transmitters must not be mounted close to sensitive receivers or delicate instruments placed in the motor compartment.

The weight of instrumentation was not important with the German rocket for that missile had been designed to carry a payload of relatively dense material, the high explosive warhead weighing one ton. However, space was a limiting factor (Fig. 3.8), because physical instruments have not a comparable overall density. Early rockets often used lead ballast in order to keep the centre of gravity well forward of the centre of pressure in order to preserve aerodynamic stability. Later attempts, notably by the Air Force, were made to improve the available space from 16·5 cubic feet (0·47 cu. metres) to 80 cubic feet (2·26 cu. metres). This was in Project Blossom in which the Air Force used part of a new supersonic aircraft as the nose-cone. It was hoped that the warhead could be brought down complete by a parachute.[16]

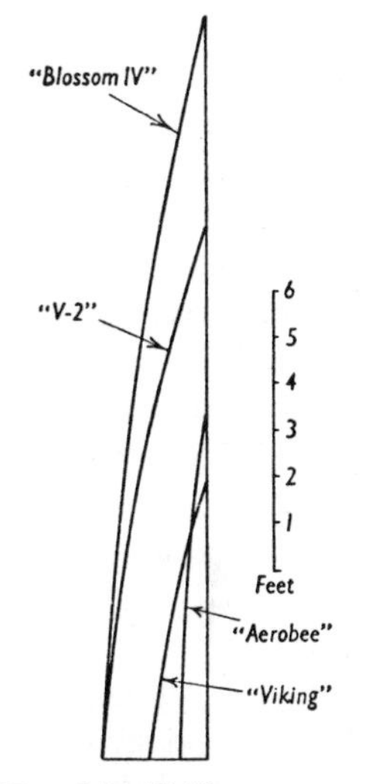

FIG. 3.8—Half nose-cones of high-altitude rockets showing the space available for instrumentations.

The Aerobee is so much smaller than the V-2 and consequently easier to construct and fire that it has many advantages. Two men, for example, can carry the empty rocket. Its small payload of 160 pounds (73 kg.) occupies about half of the available space in the missile and the relative low cost (£10,000 compared with over £100,000 for the Viking) means that it is economical to instrument only a few experiments for each shot. The Aerobee actually takes several different forms; one design, known as the Aerobee-Hi, was developed by the Air Force using helium pressurization propellent feed, to improve the mass ratio, together with a 4,000 pound (1,800 kg.) thrust motor. It was able to reach altitudes greater than the Aerobees employed by other agencies.

Currently under development is a new high-altitude sounding rocket which has an improved mass ratio over that of the Aerobee and is designed to reach even greater altitudes.

In the case of the Viking, the payload is adjustable over a range of values, and the provisional specification called for a rocket which could carry 2,000 pounds (900 kg.) to 80 miles (130 km.) or 100 pounds (45 kg.) to 135 miles (220 km.) without becoming unstable. Accordingly Viking rockets vary, but up to and including number 11 (fired before 1st June, 1954) the peak altitude reached was 158 miles (255 km.).

The first Viking was launched to a peak altitude of 50·4 miles (81 km.) on 3rd May, 1949.[17] The low altitude was caused by the premature cut-off of the propellent valves. This same trouble marred the second launching but it was later eliminated and Viking number 4, launched from the U.S.S. *Norton Sound* in mid-Pacific on 11th May, 1950, carried over half a ton of instruments to an altitude of 106·4 miles (170 km.). This launching was Project Reach of the U.S. Navy (Fig. 3.9).

A new French high-altitude rocket known as the Veronique (Fig. 3.11) is now being developed by the Laboratoires de Recherches Ballistiques et Aeronautiques, Vernon. This is the only non-American high-altitude research rocket of which details are available and twenty-five of them had been fired to mid-1953 using a novel cable launching control system which obviates the need for a launching tower. The propellents used are nitric acid and gasolene, giving a thrust of four tons for a period of 36 seconds. The rocket carries 110 pounds (50 kg.) of payload and is 19 feet 8 inches (6 metres) in length, 21 inches (55 cm.) in diameter, and weighs about one ton. The peak altitude has been in the region of 37 miles (60 km.) but there are possibilities of extending this to 80 miles (125 km.). The instrumented nose-cone is separated by an explosive charge and recovered by a drag-ring type of parachute (Fig. 3.10). Data are also telemetered by means of a 22-channel system using a transmitter operating at 52 Mc/s. The French upper-atmosphere programme with this rocket started in the Sahara Desert launching grounds in 1954.*

With all high-altitude rockets the initial problem, of course, is the recovery of data, for the solution of which two methods are possible. The first is the physical recovery of the records from the wreckage of the rocket after impact, while the other is to telemeter instrument readings back to the ground station during the flight. These two methods are quite obviously restricted to different types of experiment while sometimes, where possible, data are obtained by both methods as a check; for example, cosmic-ray counts were recorded by telemetered data and photographic film in one V-2 instrumentation. At other times data may be recorded on magnetic tape within the rocket as well as being telemetered. Magnetic tape has been recovered when broken into small strips by the impact yet has still yielded valuable data when pieced together.

* A peak of 86 miles (135 km.) was reached in February.

(*a*) Take-off showing the jet deflector and the cable control arms. The rocket is attached by four cables from the extremities of these arms passing over pulleys on the launching table and then to a controlling drum. This overcomes the need for a launching tower.

(*b*) The rocket rises still controlled by the cables.

(*c*) It reaches a speed sufficient to ensure aerodynamic stability then explosive bolts allow the launching gear to be jettisoned.

FIG. 3.11—The Veronique, French high-altitude rocket.

(*Photos., Service E. A. Propulsion*)

FIG. 3.12—The after body of a V-2 rocket located after impact. Note that it is in quite good condition so that some instruments can be mounted in this part of the rocket and safely recovered after impact.

(Photo., Naval Research Laboratory)

FIG. 3.13—A research and development type of FM-FM telemetering system with features which facilitate rapid change of measurement schedule including up to 18 frequency bands. Developed by the Jet Propulsion Laboratory Caltech.

(Photo., Courtesy C. I. Cummings and A. W. Newberry)

FIG. 3.14—A miniature PWM-PM airborne telemetering unit produced by the Applied Science Corporation, Princeton. The power unit is on the right.

(Photo., courtesy C. I. Cummings and A. W. Newberry)

FIG. 3.18—Nose section of Viking No. 1 showing Naval Research Laboratory equipment and the programme timer.

Photo. Glenn L. Martin Co. Courtesy, 'The Engineer')

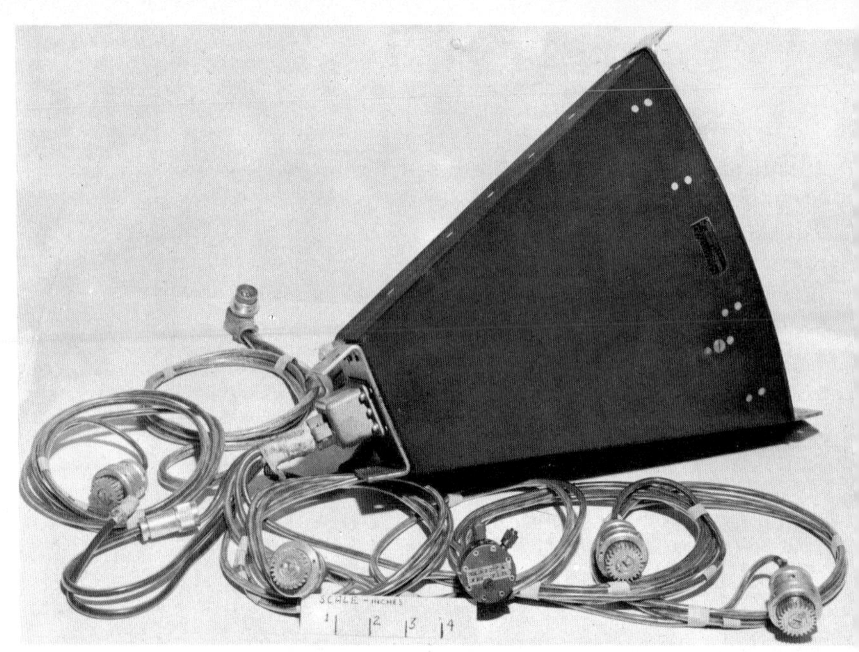

(*a*) A six-channel FM-FM telemetering system.

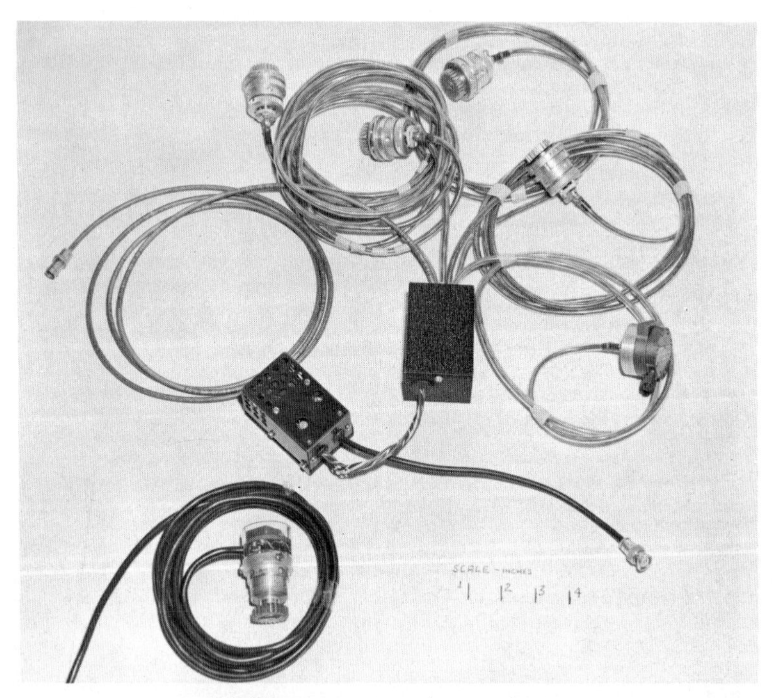

(*b*) The same system using transistors.

FIG. 3.17—Transistorizing of telemetering equipment.
(*Photos., courtesy C. I. Cummings and A. W. Newberry*)

Some data obviously cannot be telemetered, photographs of solar spectra and of the Earth, for example, and a method had to be found at an early stage for the safe recovery of such photographic films. Normally the fins on a high-altitude rocket will bring it into a nose-down attitude as it re-enters the dense lower atmosphere on the downward leg of the flight. Without losing much speed it will plunge into the Earth and dig a deep crater. V-2s, for example, disturb the soil down to 80 feet (24 metres) and produce a crater some 50 feet (15 metres) deep, even without an explosive warhead. However, by breaking up the missile as it enters the lower regions of the atmosphere, the parts can be made to have poor aerodynamic properties which causes a reduction in the impact speeds. This desirable result is accomplished by blowing off the warhead in the case of the V-2 and the Viking, or the tail skirt in the case of the Aerobee, though nowadays most Aerobee instrument cones are brought safely down by ribbon parachute. The two parts of the broken rocket tumble to Earth and are usually recovered in a fairly good condition (Fig. 3.12). One spectrograph has, for instance, been flown several times.

But most of the measurements made in upper-air research can be telemetered to the ground station during the process of the experiment. The sequence of operation is divided into three main stages. First the data must be measured, encoded and transmitted. Then it is received at the ground station. Finally, the received signals are decoded and recorded for analysis.

The first telemetering equipment was made hurriedly from equipment available at that time in 1946 when the upper-atmosphere rocket programme commenced. This was necessary for it was known that the V-2s would deteriorate with storage and should be used as quickly as possible. Essentially the measuring and transmitting consisted of converting the instrument readings to voltages and periodically sampling these for transmission on a multi-channel pulse-modulated system. This airborne unit is shown in schematic form in Fig. 3.15. A master keyer, in the form of a freely running multivibrator* with constant period, generated the first trigger impulse for each period of the data sampling. Then the vibrator for each

* A multivibrator is a resistance-coupled two-stage amplifier in which the output is returned as input to the first stage. Multivibrators can operate over a range of frequencies from 1 c/s to 100 kc/s by varying the resistance and capacitance in the circuit.

channel triggered the next one until the complete sequence of twenty-three channels had been sampled. The recovery time for any one multivibrator is controlled by the data voltage being sampled, so that the time interval between the pulses is the measure of the instrument voltages and, consequently, of the quantities they were representing. When all the channels had been transmitted, the circuit remained quiescent until the master keyer initiated the sequence once again. The original sets had a peak radio frequency power of 700 watts at 1,000 Mc/s, but these were later improved to give 1 kw. output.

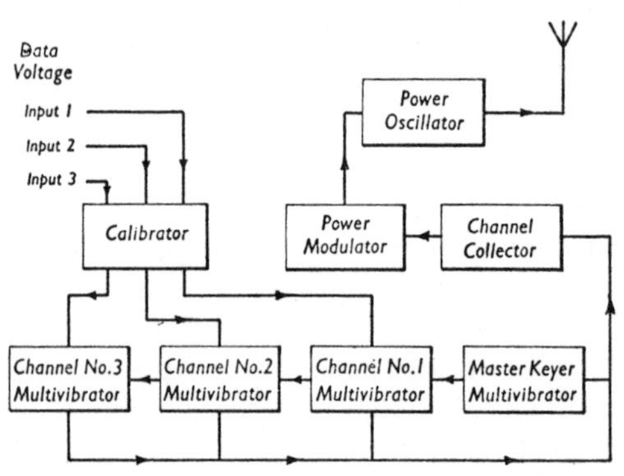

FIG. 3.15—Naval Research Laboratory airborne telemetering, schematic of transmitter.
(*Courtesy, 'The Engineer'*)

Calibration of all the equipment is important because constants are likely to change during the flight. In this connexion it is, of course, most advantageous to have voltage-stabilized power supplies. For calibration it is usual to break periodically the connexion between the data voltage source and the airborne modulator channels and to substitute controlled potentials, for example zero and a reference voltage of 3½ volts. Apparatus such as radio equipment which has to operate at high voltages, cannot work unprotected at high altitudes because of the low atmospheric pressure. This would give rise to corona discharge and arc-over and accordingly such apparatus must be enclosed in pressurized compartments.

The ground station as first employed in this early telemetering system was a mobile one and consisted of two complete stations mounted in towed trailers with power generating vehicles. In addition to the 1,000 Mc/s receiver, a video amplifier, and a decoding unit, each trailer contained recording and testing equipment and communication sets for maintaining contact with base and the blockhouse. There were also accurate timing devices.

These two mobile stations received, decoded and recorded the data transmitted from the rockets. Their aerials were mounted with servo motors so that they could follow the missiles, controlled to do so either by the optical trackers or by a radio signal maximizing system.

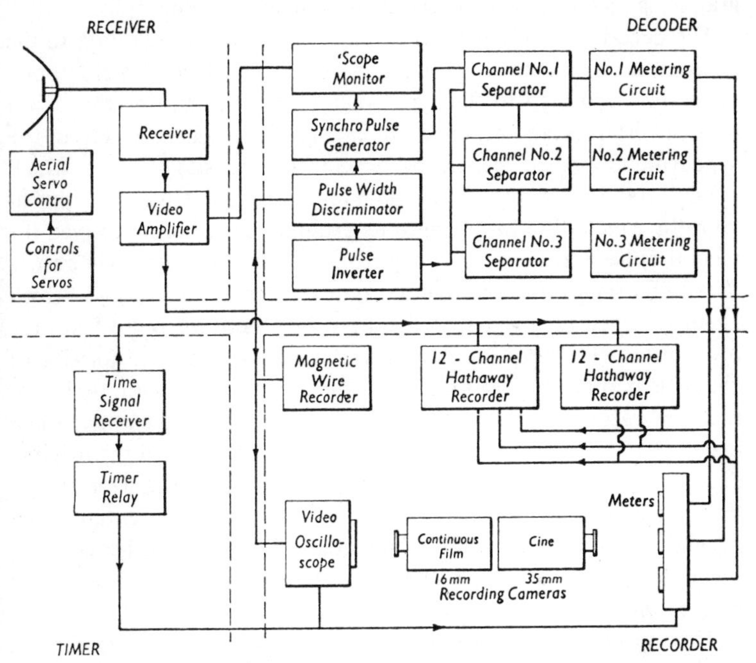

FIG. 3.16—Schematic of Naval Research Laboratory telemetering ground station.

(*Courtesy*, *'The Engineer'*)

Later a complete building was constructed to contain the ground station which thus became a permanent feature of the proving grounds.

Fig. 3.16 illustrates the sequence of operation of the ground station. The received signal was amplified and detected and then passed through suitable amplifiers to a decoder. This apparatus re-created the original data voltages from the time-modulated signals which were being received. These voltages were then used to operate meters for each of the channels and the bank of meters was photographed with a 35 mm. ciné camera. In order to prevent loss of vital data should the recorder fail, several different systems of recording were simultaneously used. The output of the video amplifier was fed on to magnetic tape and also, through an oscilloscope, it was recorded by means of a 16 mm. continuous film camera. The channel outputs from the decoder were also registered on a moving strip of photographic paper by means of Hathaway string oscillographs.

The decoder itself had a very similar sequence of operation to the transmitter. The incoming pulses were fed to a synchronizing pulse generator, and also to the input of a channel separator through a pulse inverter. At the beginning of each group of pulses received, the synchronizing pulse generator developed one single pulse which passed to the separator of channel number one and triggered a multivibrator which did not return to its ground state until it received the second pulse in the train arriving from the pulse inverter. The return of the first separator to its ground state triggered number two, which again returned to normal on the arrival of the third pulse from the transmitter. The sequence continued until the complete series of channels had been passed through. During the conduction period of each separator a constant voltage would be applied to the appropriate metering circuit for the length of time which represented the original data voltage in the rocket. By means of a suitable resistance-capacity time effect, a condenser was permitted to charge to a potential which depended upon the duration of the applied voltage and hence upon the telemetered data. A valve voltmeter was used to display the original voltage.

This system has proved quite accurate and reliable. At first, dipoles were used on both the rocket and the ground station, but it was then found that the signal would often be lost due to cross-polarization when the rocket rolled after its period of powered flight. This tumbling or spinning motion of the rocket often happens because any residual angular momentum given by the motor at the instant of cut-off cannot later be corrected, although the Viking now uses steam jets to remedy this defect. Circularly polarized tripole aerials obviated these adverse effects from bad radiation patterns.

The telemetering system has been considerably improved upon since the early rockets, and subcommutation enables many hundreds of different data samples to be transmitted. With smaller rockets simpler telemetering has to be used. In the Aerobee, for example, the first system was a frequency-modulated encoding system, used with a frequency-modulated carrier R.F. at 85 Mc/s.[18] Six channels were employed. The transmitting aerial was at the nose tip of the missile and the complete equipment, developed by the Applied Physics Laboratory, Johns Hopkins University, weighed only 20 lb. (9 kgm.). A very simple type of telemetering system was used on the Bumper-WAC by putting amplitude-modulated signals on the output of a Doppler* transmitter used for trajectory data. This equipment was remarkable in that it enabled two-way communication to be established with a missile moving at 5,150 m.p.h. (8,250 k.p.h.) and which ascended to 242 miles (390 km.) above the Earth's surface, right above the D, E, and F ionized layers of the upper atmosphere.

Further development in telemetering will include the use of transistors instead of radio valves. These make it possible for equipment which would normally occupy a volume about the size of a suitcase to be packed into less than a cigar-box. An example of this type of packaging is shown in Fig. 3.17, facing page 33.

There are certain peculiarities in rocket instrumentation which are quite independent of the type of experiment to be performed. First, experiments in rockets are much different from those which are conducted in the laboratory on the ground or in a mobile test such as in an aircraft. Once the rocket has risen from its launching platform or tower, no further correction or adjustment can be made to the test apparatus. Every smallest part of all sections of the equipment must function correctly when and after the firing button is depressed. Moreover, the failure of one section of the experiment can often invalidate or make useless data recovered from other sections. For example most rocket-measured data becomes valueless if the tracking equipment fails and the trajectory becomes unknown. Installations on rockets must accordingly be of the highest possible standard.

The success of high-altitude rocket research thus becomes an engineering problem and depends upon careful engineering and the pre-flight checking of every component which is likely to malfunction. Simplicity in design of the rocket is a great advantage, for then, if it is known that the probability of the rocket failing is low, the instrumentation is the part which has to have extra care lavished upon it. In practice it appears that simple rockets have functioned

* Cf. page 40.

best. For example the V-2, which needs a crew of about thirty people for its launching, was only about 60 per cent successful compared with the Aerobee which takes only three people to launch, and which was over 90 per cent successful taking all launchings, and 100 per cent successful taking launchings in 1953.

Secondly, the great speed of the rocket as it passes through the atmosphere, rising as it does to the ionosphere in just a few minutes, means that sampling of data must be very rapid for transmission on the telemetering system. The pulse time modulation system previously described can easily deal with rapid sampling for it can transmit at a sampling rate of 300 times per second. However, the instruments themselves have to be able to measure the data equally as rapidly. Accordingly it is often found that upper-air measurements are made indirectly by measuring things which can rapidly be determined and then calculating the parameters for these data. An example of this is that of the determination of upper-air temperature. Normal thermometers would not function and the temperature is ascertained by determining the Mach number of the rocket, the velocity of the rocket, the local velocity of sound, and hence determining the temperature.*

The rapid sampling of data in turn leads to further problems. It calls for accurate timing devices (Fig. 3.18)†. For telemetering, the measured data are correlated with trajectory data by means of a master timer mounted within the rocket and which impresses a signal on to the telemetered sequence, thus enabling the data to be plotted as an accurate function of the altitude of the rocket throughout the flight. In one design, a timing pulse was generated every half-second on a background of a 100 c/s note. This commenced at the instant of take-off and every twentieth pulse after that time was cancelled. Accurate timing was thereby ensured. In addition to electronic timers, mechanical systems have been used to control such operations as the starting of ciné and other cameras, opening of pressure gauges or sampling bottles, starting the transmitter for the ionosphere experiment, exposing spectra and controlling the cosmic-ray cloud chamber, ejecting grenades, finally operating the parachute or blowing off the warhead or tail-skirt for the air break-up. A mechanical timer, consisting of a constant-speed D.C. motor operating a camshaft through a gear chain, was used in early V-2 experiments. Five cams were mounted on the shaft and each of these operated a single-throw,

* See Chapter IV. † Between pp. 32-33.

double-pole switch. By this means not only was the equipment in the rocket operated but an indication that the switch had been thrown was transmitted on the telemetering system.

Two push-to-open tail switches were mounted in the tail of the V-2 where they were held in the open position while the rocket was on the launching table. As the rocket rose the switches closed and started the electronic and mechanical timers. Double-pole switches were again used to give a telemetered indication of the operation of the switches.

Many different agencies co-operate in the firing of a high-altitude rocket and it is the synchronization of these various participants which causes perhaps the greatest amount of trouble. High-altitude rockets cannot just be filled with propellents and then left for any length of time or else the low-temperature liquified gases start to give trouble by causing icing-up of the valves. In the case of the V-2 series the percentage of successful flights was nearly halved if the waiting time fully loaded with propellents exceeded two hours.

Hence when the word is given for the launching to take place, the instrumentation must be completed in accordance with the firing schedule. It is essential that the many months of work in all fields of instrumentation and design, in missile checking, servicing and fuelling, should culminate at the right time on the right day for the test. With the vagaries of climate, even at the desert launching sites, this problem is one of the first magnitude. Indeed high-altitude rocket experimentation places a high premium on perfection in detail, for the flight calls for co-operation between missile launching crews, instrumentation scientists, range safety personnel, recording station, radar and optical tracking stations and recovery personnel.

The rocket itself can operate badly, and become a public danger by moving out of the proving area. Telemetering is accordingly often used to monitor the performance of the rocket. In the original V-2 instrumentation, six channels were allocated to transmit details of the angular positions of the carbon control vanes, the combustion-chamber pressure and the turbine/pump speed. Data of this nature were also invaluable in determining the cause of any failure of the rocket to ascend to the height calculated or due to malfunctioning of the control system.

But passive knowledge is not enough; it is necessary to terminate the flight should the rocket approach a trajectory which would carry its impact point outside the proving area. An emergency cut-off receiver is thus employed to stop the flow of propellents to the motor. Ordinary radio receivers were used in the V-2 and as these frequency-modulated receivers had several channels they were also used as an additional safety measure to consolidate the mechanical timer's instructions for such matters as triggering the air burst.

Perhaps the most important requirement concerning the flight of a high-altitude rocket is the tracking, for upon the accuracy of this all the other measurements depend. Accordingly several different methods of tracking the rockets are used. It is necessary to know the velocity, acceleration, and altitude at all times from take-off and also the location of the plane of the trajectory. Several ways are possible of doing this.

First the distance of the rocket along its trajectory can be roughly but rapidly determined at any instant by radar ranging stations, which are particularly useful on cloudy days. Optical instruments[19, 20] were also used for tracking purposes. A fixed motion-picture camera photographed the rocket during the early stages of the trajectory at the rate of 30–180 frames a second and covered the first 34 miles (55 km.). Above an altitude of 3,000 feet (1,000 metres) a modified photo-theodolite with a focal length of up to 14 feet (4·27 metres) photographed the missile at the rate of 4 frames per second, and gave reasonable position data to heights of up to 20 miles (32 km.). For greater ranges, tracking telescopes were employed. A twin 10-inch (25·3 cm.) Cassegrain reflector was effective up to 80 miles (130 km.), while a larger 16-inch (40 cm.) Newtonian reflector (nicknamed Big Bright Eyes), mounted with a 35-mm. ciné-camera on a 90-mm. A.A. gun-base which was located at a distance of 40 miles (65 km.) from the launching apron, was able to give valuable data at 100 miles (160 km.). The rockets were painted with contrasting markings so that rotation and tumbling could be more easily observed by the optical trackers.

For velocity determination a Doppler system was employed. This depends upon the change in received frequency which is experienced when the transmitting source is moving away from or towards the observer. The system used at White Sands was known as DOVAP, Doppler, velocity and position. Two radio frequency signals are transmitted from one ground station to another, one directly and the other via the rocket. In practice at least three ground stations are

FIG. 3.19—A modified 16 mm. gun-sight camera used for determining rocket aspect.
(Photo., U.S. Navy, Courtesy, 'The Engineer')

FIG. 3.20—Photograph of the Earth taken with the wide angle camera from a height of 108 miles and used for determining the aspect of the rocket.
(Photo., U.S. Navy, Courtesy, 'The Engineer'

FIG. 3.23—Naval Research Laboratory and Martin personnel are shown putting the instrumented nose cone on to a Viking rocket.

(Photo., Glenn L. Martin Co., Courtesy, 'The Engineer')

used to increase the reliability of the data and to give the position of the missile as well as its velocity. The signal transmitted to the vehicle is at a frequency of 36·94 Mc/s. At the rocket the frequency is doubled and retransmitted. When received at the ground stations this signal then beats with the frequency doubled signal which has been received directly from the transmitting station. The resulting beat frequency enables the missile speed and the distance from the transmitter to the missile and to the receiver to be computed. The position in space can then be determined relative to the several ground receiving stations.

It has been mentioned earlier that the rocket often spins or tumbles after the period of power, and accordingly it is necessary to know its orientation throughout the flight. During power the V-2 was controlled by vanes of sintered carbon which dipped into the exhaust stream. However, any residual angular momentum at cut-off, plus the effects of high-altitude winds, could cause the rocket to roll, pitch, and yaw during the rest of the flight. The Aerobee was fin-stabilized during the powered part of the flight but was found to spin consistently after all-burnt, giving a roll rate of one revolution in just under five seconds. In the Viking rocket an attempt has been made to rectify this failing. In order to keep the rocket at a constant heading in space, steam jets are used after all the propellents have been consumed.

Knowledge of the orientation of the rocket is important if correct interpretation is to be given to the experimental results recorded by the instruments within the rocket. Orientation can be determined from the optical trackers but this is not sufficiently accurate and can be prevented if cloudy conditions prevail. The next most useful method is by photography of the Earth's surface from the rocket itself. This is a very accurate method of determining the aspect.

Fig. 3.19 shows a modified gun-sight camera flown in a Viking rocket to check orientation. An auxiliary hemispherical lens was attached to increase the field of view to about 160°. Two of the three angles needed for orientation determination were determined from the image of the Earth's horizon while the third was gained from the position of landmarks or the image of the Sun which appeared on some of the frames. Exact timing was given by means of an intermittent light which was also 'tied' to the base station through the telemetering system.[21]

The two difficulties with this system lie with the necessity for recovery of the film container and the blanketing of surface detail by clouds. Consequently if the rocket has to be fired where recovery is not possible, alternative methods have to be used. One of these is to install photo-cell aspect indicators in the rocket which will give the position of the rocket relative to the Sun. Taken in conjunction with determination of the Earth's magnetic field, these results can be telemetered with magnetometer readings. Similarly a gyro-system might also be employed, but so far there are no reports of one being used.

In some cases (notably the WAC Corporal, 2nd stage of the Bumper-WAC and the V-2 carrying cloud chambers), roll has been induced by small rocket units in order either to increase stability or to improve the operation of an experiment.

In the first series of tests using the V-2 rocket for high-altitude research the warhead was redesigned by the Naval Research Laboratory, but retained its original dimensions. The new warhead was constructed in three sections,[22] a nose-tip for temperature and pressure gauges, which was some 12 inches (30·5 cm.) long and with a base diameter of 3 inches (7·6 cm.), a nose section, 22 inches (56 cm.) long, with a maximum diameter of 12·37 inches (31 cm.) and then the main body of the warhead. The nose section was originally intended to house a spectrograph, but was later used for other equipment. The main warhead was fitted with three access doors to facilitate installation of the equipment. It was constructed from $\frac{3}{8}$-inch (9·5-mm.) cast steel and had a maximum diameter of 37·625 inches (96 cm.) and a length of 57 inches (144 cm.). With experiments designed to be operated at high altitudes where the ambient air pressure is very low, difficulties arise because the air breaks down as an insulator. Arc-over and glow discharges take place, especially from high-voltage equipment. Consequently this warhead was made so that it could be sealed at ground level to keep all the contained equipment pressurized during the flight. Cable connexions were brought through the base by special plugs which were sealed by packing glands.

In the control compartment, aft of the warhead, a large amount of space was available and this was used for such equipment as the Doppler and Doppler aerial, the emergency cut-off receiver, the telemetering transmitter, power supplies, cloud chamber, and gyroscopes for control of the rocket (Fig. 3.21).

A second design of warhead was constructed in a slightly different

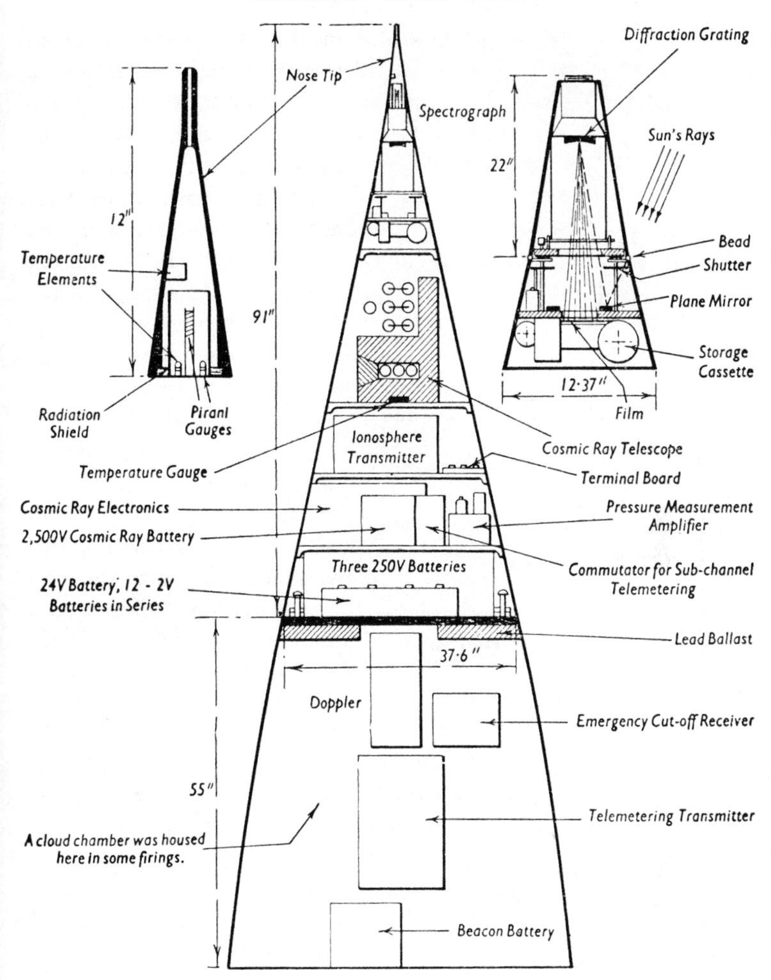

FIG. 3.21—Diagram of an early V-2 instrumentation showing the Naval Research Laboratory equipment in the rebuilt warhead.
(*Courtesy*, '*The Engineer*')

manner, it being made in two sections, a nose-cone and a main section. The cone, fabricated from $\frac{1}{8}$-inch (3-mm.) aluminium was 49·87 inches (126 cm.) in length with a base diameter of 23·87 inches (61 cm.) and was completely removable from the rest of the warhead in order to facilitate instrumentation. It could, moreover, be separately pressurized. The main section could also be pressurized and was

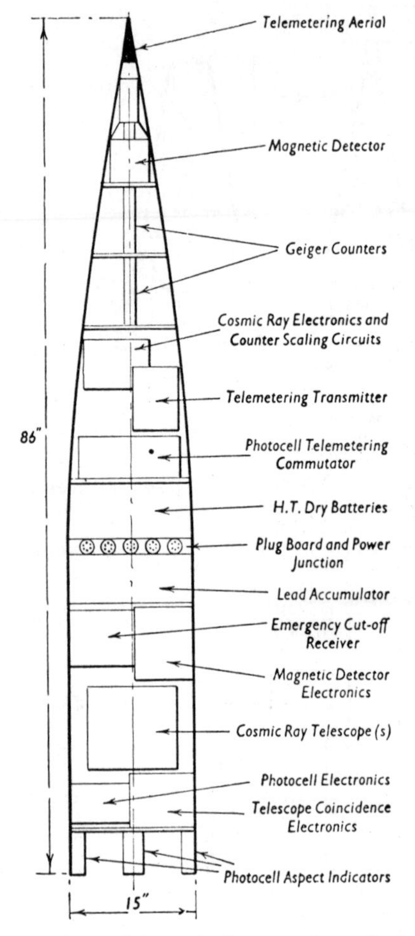

FIG. 3.22—Schematic diagram of a typical Aerobee instrumentation showing the location of instruments for a cosmic ray and magnetometer experiment.
(*Courtesy 'The Engineer'*)

of $\frac{3}{4}$-inch (1·9-cm.) pressed steel with two access doors. It was 33 inches (84 cm.) long with a maximum diameter of 37·6 inches (96 cm.). For cosmic-ray work, other warheads were designed to obviate production of showers in the material of the warhead itself. One of these, used with a large cosmic-ray telescope in the experiment of 10th July, 1947, was constructed almost entirely of aluminium. As the experiments proceeded warheads were designed to suit the kind of research associated with the firing concerned. This practice is now followed and examples of various instrumentations are shown in Figs. 3.22, 4.7, 4.8, 4.10, 4.16.

Two serious objections are raised by the use of rockets for upper-atmosphere research. The first is concerned with the cost of the vehicle and its firing even without instrumentation, and the fact that these vehicles can only be sent up from a few launching grounds throughout the world. The second problem is associated with the short time of stay of the rockets in the high-altitude regions. This latter problem is so very important that it will have a complete chapter devoted to it later in this book when it will be shown that it is capable of solution by the creation of instrumented Earth-satellite vehicles.

But the problem of cost and restricted launching bases has also been partially solved. Dr. J. A. Van Allen, head of the Rocket Panel, searched for an inexpensive way of reaching high altitudes and found it in a combination of balloon and rocket. He realized that there are a number of solid-propellent military rockets which if fired in a vacuum would have all-burnt velocities in the region of 2,750 miles per hour (4,400 km./hr.) which could carry them to a peak altitude of 50 miles (80 km.) if air resistance were neglected. He solved the problem of getting the small rockets to an altitude of 10 miles (16 km.) where air resistance is low, by hanging them from a line, 100 feet (31 metres) beneath a Skyhook plastic balloon. The balloon ascent took about an hour to accomplish and then the rocket, a modified Deacon military rocket, was fired by remote radio command. The solid propellent rocket burns for 3½ seconds and accelerates at about 60g. carrying up to 60 pounds (27·5 kg.) payload to an altitude (in August 1953) of 50 miles (80 km.). The nose compartment was pressurized and data were telemetered by a 76 Mc/s signal. Data measured with this apparatus have included cosmic radiation, pressure and temperature, sky brightness, airglow and solar X-rays. Rockets can be launched anywhere on the Earth, providing range safety (dispersal of up to 30 miles [50 km.] radius) is complied with. The cost of the rocket and balloon (the Rockoon) is in the region of only £420. Rockets of this nature could be used from aircraft also [23] for synoptic observations of the upper atmosphere and solar and cosmic-ray physics.

With rockets then, we have a vehicle capable of carrying instruments into all regions of the Earth's atmosphere. The lower part of the atmosphere, that is up to 50 miles (80 km.) or so, can be probed by Rockoons and aircraft-launched rockets or vehicles similar to the WAC Corporal. These can investigate such phenomena as the temperature minimum, the ozone layers, seasonal variation of winds, the lowest ionized layer and make certain cosmic-ray experiments.

For the region from 50 miles to 90 miles (80–150 km.) rockets like the Aerobee are needed. These can undertake work such as the investigation of ionization processes in the atmosphere, diffusive separation of the gases, E layer ionization, solar spectroscopy into the far ultra-violet, sky light and airglow, auroral current sheets, electrojets, auroral corpuscles and cosmic radiation.

Finally, for the outer regions of the atmosphere, larger rockets such as the Viking, or step rockets like the Bumper-WAC, become essential. Work will include solar radiation, cosmic rays, high-altitude winds, formation of the F layers, diffusive separation, ionization and photo-chemical effects of the solar radiation, impact of extra-terrestrial particles on the upper atmosphere, for example interplanetary dust (micrometeorites), and corpuscular streams from the Sun. In all these three regions, data concerning the composition, temperature, pressure and density of the upper atmosphere will be gathered. This will be especially important in the two higher regions where considerable differences of opinion now range as to the true values to be found.

We have seen how far man reached before he had rockets, we have seen how high he can reach with present rocket vehicles, now it is possible to examine the type of results which have been obtained and find out how the ground-based and rocket-based measurements compare with each other.

REFERENCES

[1] GODDARD, R. H., *A Method of Reaching Extreme Altitudes*, Smithsonian Institute Publication, 2540, 1919

[2] OBERTH, H., *Wege zur Raumschiffahrt*, R. Oldenbourg, 1929

[3] LEY, W., SCHAEFER, H., *L'Aerophile*, Oct. 1936

[4] MALINA, F. J., SMITH, A. M., *Jnl. Aeron. Sc.*, **5**, 199, 1938. Research and Development at the Jet Propulsion Laboratory, GALCIT, *Jnl. Brit. Interpl. Soc.*, **6**, 34, 1946, *Jnl. Americ. Rocket Soc.*, No. 66/7, 1946

[5] *Naval Research Laboratory Report R-2955, Upper Atmosphere Report No.* 1, 1946

[6] PERRING, W. G. A., *Jnl. Roy. Aeron. Soc.*, **50**, 483, 1946

[7] KOOY, J. M. J., UYTENBOGAART, J. W. H., *Ballistics of the Future*, Ch. VI, Stam Publishing Co., 1946

[8] VAN ALLEN, J. A., FRAZER, L. W., FLOYD, J. F. R., *Science*, **108**, 746, 1948

[9] SEIFERT, H. S., MILLS, M. M., SUMMERFIELD, M., *Amer. Jnl. of Phys.*, **15**, 121–140, 1947

[10] SUTTON, G. P., *Rocket Propulsion Elements*, Wiley, 1949

[11] BURGESS, E., *Rocket Propulsion*, Chapman & Hall, 1952

[12] *Journal of the American Rocket Society*, 1934 to date

[13] GATLAND, K. W., *Jnl. Brit. Interpl. Soc.*, **7**, 160, 1948

[14] SEIFERT, H. S., MILLS, M. M., SUMMERFIELD, M., *loc. cit.* 9

[15] HAVILAND, R. P., *Report of the Bumper Programme*, Amer. Museum Nat. History, Off. Release, Oct. 1951

[16] O'DAY, M., *Proc. 11th Intern. Cong. Appl. Mechs.* 2, Part II, 515, 1948

[17] LAYTON, J. P., *Americ. Rocket Soc. Convention*, 1950

[18] MELTON, G. H., *Electronics*, **21**, 106, 1948

[19] REVYL, D., *Sky & Telescope*, 299, Oct. 1949

[20] MANN, M., *Ordnance*, **33**, 23, 1948

[21] ROSEN, M. W., Naval Research Laboratory, Priv. Comm. 1952

[22] Naval Research Laboratory, *loc. cit.*, 5

[23] SINGER, S. F., *Nature*, **171**, 1108, 1953

higher absorbing layers, namely radiation of wavelengths greater than about 2,900A. These regions are characterized by considerable turbulence and mixing of the atmosphere and the formation of clouds. In the upper atmosphere, on the other hand, only rarely are clouds seen, and these are limited to the noctilucent ones at a height of about 50 miles (80 km.) or so. Yet this region is in many cases more interesting than the troposphere, for whereas the latter is the region in which condensation produces the wonderful cloud effects which complete any landscape, in the upper air the solar radiations act on the individual atoms and molecules of the atmosphere. The operative radiation is in the ultra-violet range of the solar spectrum, that is at wavelengths less than 3,000A, and this radiation is capable of causing electrons to be freed from their orbits thus producing ionization. In some cases and at great heights it is sufficiently intense to split the molecules of oxygen and nitrogen so that these elements then exist in the atomic form. Accordingly the upper region of the atmosphere is one of excitation and ionization, photo-dissociation and allotropic modification of the atmospheric gases. It is almost like a great photochemical laboratory in which processes difficult or even impossible to reproduce in the laboratories on the Earth's surface, are carried out daily, some of them making possible the continuance of life on Earth, others, as we shall see, interfering with man's technical developments and his communications. Doubtless some of these upper-air phenomena also influence weather conditions in the troposphere and their complete understanding will help meteorologists in the difficult task of long-range weather forecasting.

The physical properties of the upper atmosphere, namely, temperature, pressure, density, and composition, have been very much in dispute since man first began investigating these high regions. Before the use of high-altitude rockets no direct measurements of the air temperature above 22 miles (35 km.) had been made. But this did not imply ignorance of the temperature to be expected. Calculations were based on such factors as the absorption of solar energy by the ozone layers,[1] atmospheric tides,[2] the explosion of [3] and the brightness and the velocity of meteors,[4] the spectrum of the aurorae,[5] and the behaviour of radio waves in the ionized layers,[6] and we have noted earlier how the anomalous propagation of sound waves indicated a high-temperature region at an altitude of around 34 miles (55 km.). While it had been known for some time that the temperature in the stratosphere was quite low compared with sea-level conditions, some of the upper-air calculations indicated extremely high temperatures, approaching and exceeding 1,000° K.

The result of all this theoretical work was the establishment of the temperature gradient to great atitudes. In the troposphere the tem-

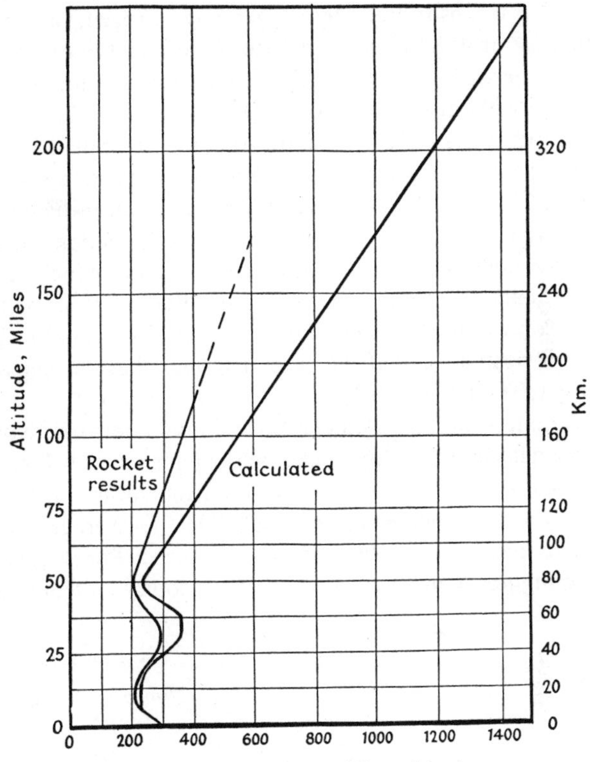

FIG. 4.1—Temperature °K. *v.* altitude.

perature drops steadily from sea level at the rate of about 1° K. for each 540 feet (160 metres) of altitude until the stratospheric temperature of 220° K. is reached. This remains roughly constant, except in the equatorial stratosphere, until about 19 miles (30 km.)—varying with latitude—and then it begins to increase. A maximum is reached at around 30 to 37 miles (50–60 km.) when a temperature of 350° K. is postulated for the anomalous propagation of sound waves. This peak is caused by the absorption of energy by the ozone,[1, 7] and it is higher than the main ozone layer because the maximum energy absorption takes place above the densest part of the layer.

Higher still, the temperature falls again and reaches a minimum value of about 240° K. at an altitude of 50 miles (80 km.) where the noctilucent clouds form. From that point it increases once more, this time due to absorptions by oxygen and nitrogen,[8] and the rise continues, as far as can be ascertained, right into the outer regions of the exosphere. At 75 miles (120 km.) the temperature is 400° K., at 275 miles (440 km.), it is 1,600° K. (Fig. 4.1).

The temperatures in the outer regions are computed in several different ways. First an estimate can be made from the aurorae which occur from 50 miles (80 km.) to 700 miles (1,100 km.) which indicate temperatures above 1,000° K. Then there is the formation and equilibrium of the uppermost ionized layers, which indicate high temperatures, and finally there is the question of the disappearance of helium. This question will be discussed more fully later, but from this lack of helium it is postulated that the exosphere must have a temperature of at least 1,500° K. (Fig. 4.1).

Unfortunately, all these temperatures do not compare favourably with those determined by the rocket measurements, as will presently be discussed, so that, at the moment, the temperature of the higher regions of the atmosphere is somewhat in doubt. Averages of rocket experiments have been published by the Rocket Panel[9] giving the following figures compared with the previously accepted values (Table 4.1):

TABLE 4.1 *Upper-air Temperatures*

Altitude *miles*	*km.*	*Theoretical temperature* °K.	*Rocket Panel temperature* °K.
31–37*	50–60	360	270
50†	80	240	203
75	120	400	270
140	220	800	455

* Layer of maximum temperature. † Layer of minimum temperature.

Radio measurements based on collisional frequencies* and scale heights,† and which demand high temperatures in the ionosphere, seem to be at variance with the rocket measurements, but most recent auroral spectral studies by Petrie[10] indicate values of 750–850° K. in the 125 miles (200 km.) region. This is something of a compromise

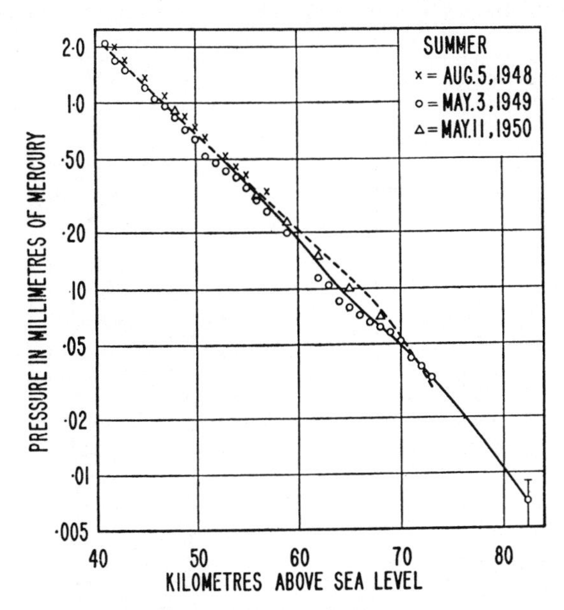

FIG. 4.2—Measurements of pressure *v.* altitude for summer months.

(*Courtesy, N.R.L. and Pergamon Press*)

between the temperatures required by the rocket data and those demanded from radio studies of the ionized regions. It is important to note that, in the temperature determinations, if the mean molecular weight is taken as being too high, low temperatures will result. It

* The collisional frequency in the ionized layer is determined from the absorption of the radio waves. It can also be calculated from the temperature and pressure. Hence by making assumptions concerning the pressure it is possible to calculate the temperature from the radio measurements.

† The scale height = $k. T/\text{m.g.}$ where k = Boltzmann's constant, T is the temperature, m, the molecular mass, and g = acceleration of gravity.

may be that the rocket data are based on molecular weights which are not correct or that the other measurements are based on molecular weights which are really lower than the true ones. In this respect it is to be expected that there will be disagreement between different authorities because there is a measure of doubt in the region above 60 miles (100 km.) arising from lack of knowledge of precisely at what height the oxygen molecules are dissociated and when all the

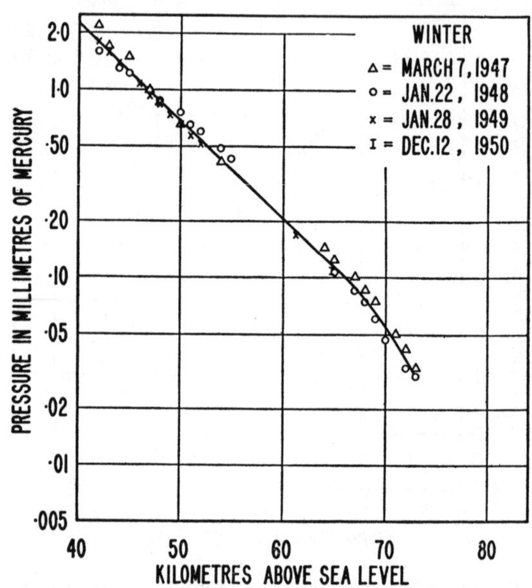

FIG. 4.3—Measurements of pressure *v.* altitude for winter months.
(Courtesy, N.R.L. and Pergamon Press)

oxygen in the atmosphere is found in the atomic form. But measurements of solar X-rays between 1,425 and 1,650A have shown that oxygen is definitely dissociating at a height of 60 miles (100 km.).[11]

If the ionosphere is a region in which the absolute temperature is not finally determined, the exosphere temperature is even more in doubt. Some theories suggest that the temperature gradually rises as the atmosphere tails off into the interplanetary gas, finally reaching a value equal to that of the gas, namely, 10,000–15,000° K. as estimated by Spitzer.[12] Other hypotheses[13] assume outer region temperatures of 1,800° K. and 2,500° K. for an isothermal region in which particles of the Earth's atmosphere move in free orbits in the gravitational field.

The pressure (Figs. 4.2, 4.3) and the density (Fig. 4.4) fall off rapidly in value with increasing height. At the summit of Mount Everest, for example, the pressure is one-third of the sea-level value. At the top of the stratosphere, the pressure is one three-thousandth

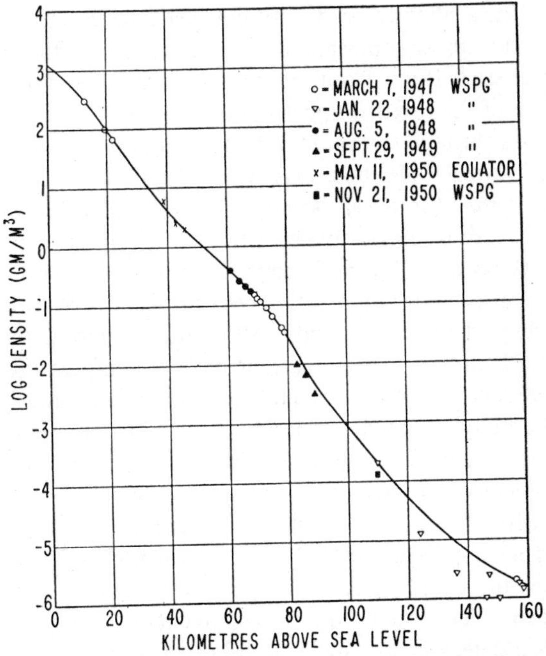

FIG. 4.4—Density *v.* altitude for a number of rocket flights.
(Courtesy, Naval Research Laboratory)

of the sea-level value, while in the upper regions, pressures as low as one thousand-millionth (at 220 km.) of that at sea level are experienced. Similarly, density falls from a particle concentration of $2{\cdot}6 \times 10^{19}$ particles per cubic centimetre at the bottom of the atmosphere, to $2{\cdot}6 \times 10^{9}$ particles per cubic centimetre at 190 miles (300 km.). The mean free path (that is, the average distance travelled by a molecule of the atmospheric gases between successive collisions with other molecules) varies from one-millionth of a centimetre at sea level to one kilometre at an altitude of 140 miles (220 km.) and over 60 miles (100 km.) at a height of 300 miles (500 km.). A problem arises in this connexion, for if the mean free path is in the neighbourhood of 60 miles (100 km.) at altitudes above 190 miles (300 km.) this would mean that the gases would diffuse very rapidly and it is accordingly difficult to account for the stability of the ionized layer at 200 miles (320 km.). This is a problem which may be solved when high-altitude rockets can be fired into these upper regions.

Rockets have already been carrying instruments into the lower regions of the upper atmosphere in order to clarify the details of its characteristics. It is, of course, impossible to measure directly the temperature of the rarefied upper atmosphere. In the first place, the rocket passes through so rapidly that a thermometer would have no time in which to stabilize and register the temperature of each region passed through. Moreover, the normal thermometer registers temperature because of convective heat transfer from its surroundings. However, above an altitude of about 37 miles (60 km.) heat transfer by convection becomes inoperative because there is so little air, the main heating effect on any body in the atmosphere at that height would arise from the solar radiations and the temperature reached by it would depend not upon the temperature of the atmosphere but on how the body accepted or rejected these solar radiations, that is, for example, whether it was painted black or white. In addition there is the problem of aerodynamic heating of the rocket at the high speeds involved, the skin of the V-2, for example, has been known to heat up to a temperature of 472° K. while in flight.

However, the temperature of the upper-atmospheric gases can be computed in several ways from measurements of other parameters. The first is a determination of the absolute pressure, but as this may be masked by gases emanating from the rocket itself, a better method is to determine the temperature from the ratio between the nose-tip and nose-cone wall pressures using the Mach number theory. This has the added attraction that the absolute pressure can be more accurately determined from the temperature data, than the temperature can be determined from the pressure.

Temperature measurements by rockets are accordingly made indirectly from pressure measurements or the comparison of pressures on different parts of the nose-cone. Hence rockets are fitted with pressure gauges to measure the pressure at various regions of the rocket surface (Fig. 4.5).

Originally the upper-air pressure measurements were divided into three main sections. These comprised three definite ranges of pressure. The first was from atmospheric pressure of 760 mm. of mercury down to only a few millimetres of mercury. In this range[14] the measurements were made with simple bellows gauges actuating microtorque potentiometers. Then, from a few millimetres of mercury down to a hundredth of a millimetre, pressures were measured by

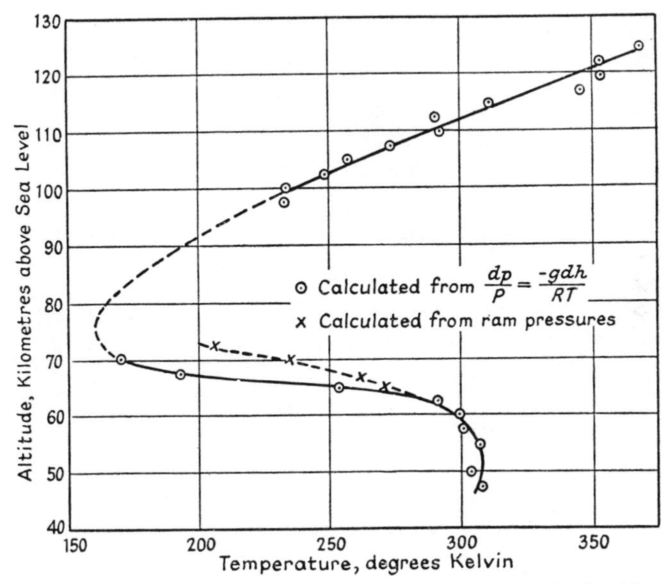

FIG. 4.5—A typical curve of temperature *v.* altitude obtained with a high-altitude rocket.

(*Courtesy, Naval Research Laboratory*)

means of Pirani gauges.[15] This type of gauge operates on the principle that heat conducted from a hot wire depends upon the pressure of the ambient gas if the mean free path of the molecules is of the same order of magnitude as the diameter of the wire. The resistance of the wire depends also on its temperature, so that the potential difference across the heated filament can be made to vary with ambient pressure. A variable potential difference can be easily telemetered and hence this gauge was very useful.

German wind-tunnel data had indicated that the best place to mount such gauges for the determination of absolute pressure would be just ahead of the tail fins on the V-2 because in that region of the rocket's skin, ambient pressure of the surrounding atmosphere should be measured within about 5 per cent of its true value. The bellows gauges were also mounted in this region.

The third section covered pressures from 10^{-2} to 10^{-7} mm. Hg. For this, ionization gauges were employed.[16] Essentially these consisted of small thermionic valves with a connexion between the

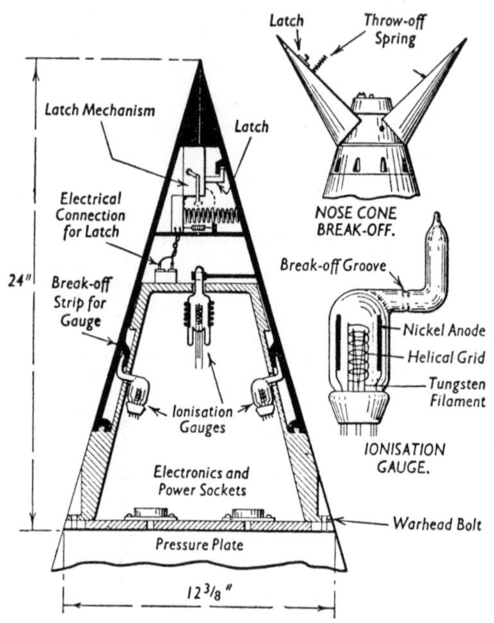

FIG. 4.6—An example of a pressure measuring nose-cone instrumentation as used in the University of Michigan experiments.
(*Courtesy*, '*The Engineer*')

interior of the envelope and the outside of the rocket. A heated filament, or a cold cathode emitter, acted as a source of electrons which flowed to the positive grid. If the electrons hit any of the atoms of the atmosphere and the charge on the electron multiplied by the ionization potential of the gas was exceeded by the kinetic energy of the electron, the gas atoms would become ionized. The released electrons would join the stream to the grid and add to the grid current, while the positive ions were attracted to the negatively charged anode which was at 3,000 volts with respect to the cathode. The path from cathode to anode was lengthened by using a magnetic field crossing the electric field and causing the electrons to move along helical paths. With this instrument the high anode voltage necessitated mounting in a pressurized section of the rocket, otherwise arc-over would have taken place. Accordingly it was not possible to use such gauges in the tail section; instead they were mounted in the pressurized nose cone (Fig. 4.6). Calibrations of the gauges prior to flight tests showed that the variations of grid and anode currents were accurate indications of the ambient pressure. In flight, the gauges had to be protected from the dense air at low altitudes and they were sealed after calibration. The glass tubulation seal was broken during the rocket's flight by a timing device when the ambient pressure had fallen to a value low enough for the gauges to operate. One important fact concerning this type of gauge is that it is insensitive to acceleration, while the Pirani gauge is not.

Four ionization gauges were used in the early V-2 work and they were arranged around the nose-cone so that ram pressure which may be built up by pitching or yawing of the rocket would be readily detected and allowed for in the results. A comparison between the cone wall pressure gauges and a fifth, forward, ram-pressure gauge, enabled the Mach number to be calculated from the Taylor-Maccoll theory. By making assumptions regarding the atmospheric constituents it was then possible to compute the atmospheric temperature.

The early part of a rocket flight of this nature is usually checked by instruments in meteorological balloons both before and after the rocket launching, and the temperature at high altitudes is determined by numerical integration from the pressure data using the peak balloon measurements as an integration constant.

Since the early work, new types of pressure gauge have been developed, and other rockets have carried them aloft, namely the Aerobee and the Viking. Havens[17] has designed a gauge capable of measuring pressures through the range from one atmosphere to less than 10^{-5} mm Hg. The pressure is cyclically changed in two recording compartments and the frequency of the change in pressure is governed by a small electric motor. The gauge produces an A.C. signal which is determined by the pressure. In the new gauge the detecting elements can be Pirani or ionization gauges which are placed inside sylphon brass bellows of 6 c.c. capacity. Two such bellows are driven

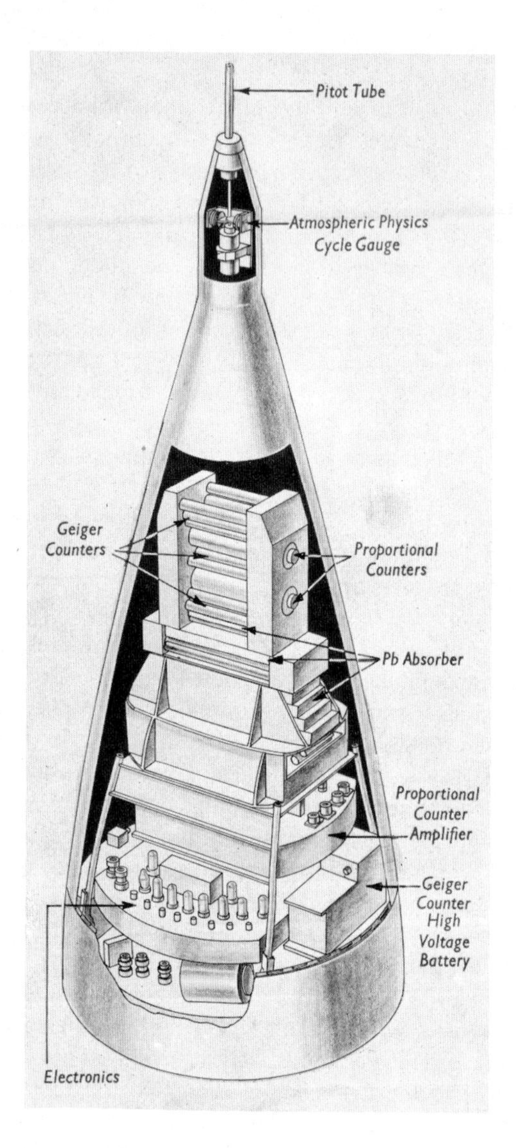

FIG. 4.7—Diagram of the instruments in the nose-cone of Viking No. 4 showing the cosmic ray telescope and the cyclical pressure gauge.

(Courtesy, Naval Research Laboratory and 'The Engineer')

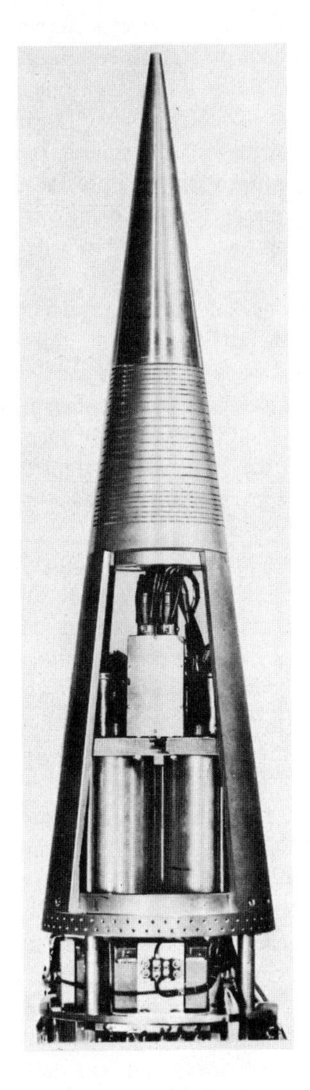

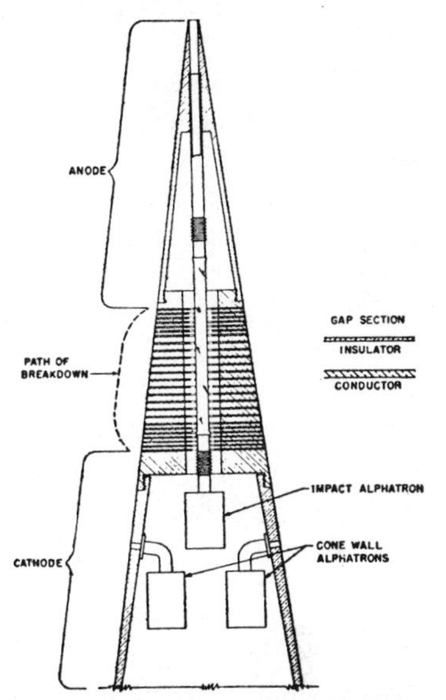

(*b*) Cross-sectional diagram of the nose-cone, illustrating the positions of anode and cathode and the breakdown path.
(*Photo., University of Michigan, Courtesy, Pergamon Press*)

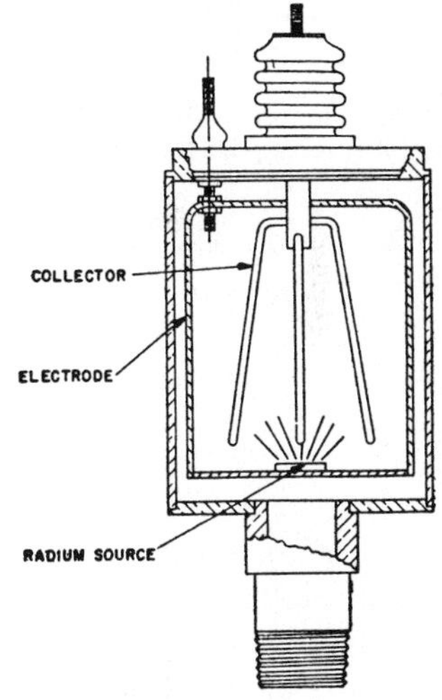

FIG. 4.8

(*a*) Photograph of a nose-cone of a rocket designed to use a voltage breakdown method for determining air density.
(*Photo., University of Michigan*)

(*c*) Diagram of alphatron gauge showing constructional features.
(*Photo., University of Michigan, Courtesy, Pergamon Press*)

by the electric motor through an eccentric shaft which can change their volume by about 20 per cent. The ambient pressure is communicated to the inside of the bellows by small holes which are dimensioned so as to pass gas at a speed sufficient to allow for the fall in pressure with the rising of the rocket through the atmosphere, but not quickly enough to follow the relatively rapid variations produced by the motor. On a Viking rocket, the gauge was used to measure pressures from 760 mm. Hg at ground level to $5{\cdot}7 \times 10^{-4}$ mm. Hg at 32 miles (53 km.) altitude (Fig. 4.7).

Another type of pressure-sensitive gauge is the 'alphatron' which is really an ionization gauge employing alpha particles, from a radioactive source, as the ionizing agents. Alphatrons have been used in University of Michigan experiments and have superseded the thermionic ionization gauges. Below 50 miles (80 km.) they perform as pressure gauges, and above that altitude they operate as density gauges. They have been flown in Aerobee rockets up to peaks of 55 miles (90 km.) and have been most successful.

Density has also been determined by University of Michigan workers using a voltage-breakdown method. The nose tip of the rocket skin was insulated from the rest of the nose-cone and a varying potential difference applied between these two surfaces. At a voltage depending upon the atmospheric density, the insulation broke down. The system operated well but the results could not be interpreted too rigidly because they applied to the atmosphere just behind the nose shock wave (Fig. 4.8).

Other methods have also been devised to determine the Mach number of the rocket. The University of Michigan used a Mach cone and determined the angle the shock wave made to the longitudinal axis of a slender cone from which the shock originated. Two cones were used, one on either side of the warhead, to give aerodynamic symmetry (Fig. 4.9). On one of them a pressure-sensitive device was mounted on an arm which oscillated backwards and forwards through the area where the shock wave was likely to be placed. The passage of the probe through the shock was measured and telemetered to the ground station together with an indication of the position of the probe itself. The angle of the shock wave was thus determined and the local Mach number computed. The local velocity of sound obtained thereby from the trajectory data made it possible for the ambient temperature to be computed.

This system was later abandoned in favour of the cone and ram pressure method, but the University of Michigan has also evolved yet a further means of upper-atmosphere temperature determination. A collapsed sphere of nylon fabric is carried aloft in an Aerobee rocket and ejected at the peak of the trajectory. Upon ejection the sphere is automatically expanded by air pressure from a small pressure bottle within it. Also contained within the sphere is a Doppler

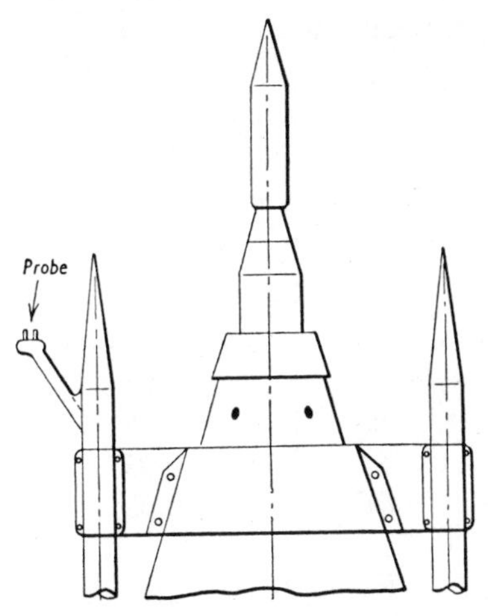

FIG. 4.9—Diagram of the mounting of the Mach cone sensing probe as used by the University of Michigan.
(*Courtesy 'The Engineer'*)

receiver and transmitter which picks up a C.W. signal of 36·94 Mc/s and retransmits at 73·88 Mc/s. Several ground stations receive the signals and pass them to a central recording station. The falling rate of the sphere can be accurately measured from the Doppler principle and accordingly it is possible to estimate the density and temperature of the atmosphere through which the sphere falls. It is expected that this method will ultimately yield very reliable data and preliminary tests have given results which are in accord with the previously-mentioned data from the Rocket Panel. Ultimately such spheres may be carried to extreme altitudes and give data concerning the exosphere which we are not likely to obtain in any other way because of the extremely low densities and pressures in that region.

The final results of the upper-air temperature work appear to confirm that there are both diurnal and seasonal variations in the upper atmosphere but that the average curves of variation of temperature with altitude are now reliable indications of upper-atmosphere conditions to heights of at least 90 miles (150 km.).

One major difficulty in the obtaining of absolute accuracy in the determination of physical properties lies in the uncertainty concerning atmospheric composition. At sea level, 99 per cent of the atmosphere consists of nitrogen and oxygen molecules with traces of other gases[18] (Table 4.2).

TABLE 4.2 *Atmospheric Composition at Sea Level*

Gas	*Symbol*	*Percentage*	*Molecular weight*
Nitrogen	N_2	78·08	28·016
Oxygen	O_2	20·95	32·000
Argon	A	0·93	39·944
Carbon dioxide ..	CO_2	0·03	44·010
Neon	Ne		20·183
Krypton	Kr		83·7
Xenon	Xe		131·3
Ozone	O_3	0·01	48·000
Helium	He		4·003
Hydrogen	H_2		2·016
Radon	Rn		222·0

At high altitudes, however, the solar radiation is found to dissociate the molecules of the atmospheric gases. The most well-known effect is that on the oxygen which is thought to commence about 50 miles (80 km.) up. Photo-dissociation of the oxygen molecule takes place strongly in the upper atmosphere by sunlight of wavelengths between 1,925 and 1,760A (the Runge-Schuman absorption bands) and more weakly by a series of absorption bands (Hertzberg continuum) beginning at 2,429A[19] and extending to 2,856A[20]. Although it is fairly definite that this process starts at about the level of the E ionized layer, i.e. 50 miles (80 km.), it is not known at what height all the molecular oxygen (molecular weight 32) is dissociated to atomic oxygen (molecular weight 16). The Rocket Panel data previously quoted is based on the assumption that dissociation starts at 50 miles (80 km.) and proceeds uniformly with increasing altitude to completion at 75 miles (120 km.).[9]

In the presence of a third body which can take up some of the energy, the atoms of oxygen may recombine or even unite with an oxygen molecule to form ozone (O_3). The ozone-producing mechanism is thus:

$$O_2 + h.v.^* \rightarrow O + O$$
$$O + O_2 + M \rightarrow O_3 + M$$

In turn, the ozone can be destroyed either by molecular collision with an oxygen molecule:

$$O + O_3 \rightarrow 2O_2$$

or by photo-dissociation resulting from solar ultra-violet radiation in the Hartley continuum from a wavelength of 3,300A to one of 2,100A, and also by infra-red radiation (Chappius continuum from 8,000A). We have seen that the ozone layer acts as a heat absorber and reservoir which raises the atmospheric temperature considerably in that region giving a peak of temperature above the densest part of the ozone layer. Assuming that the layer loses heat, due to infra-red radiation, continuously by day and night, Johnson has shown from Naval Research Laboratory studies of ultra-violet absorption, that the ozone regions experience a diurnal temperature variation having a maximum value of 5·3° K. at an altitude of 30 miles (48 km.).[21]

Nitrogen is a more difficult molecule to dissociate, but it is assumed that dissociation does begin to take place at an altitude of 75 miles (120 km.). The Rocket Panel data are based on the assumption that dissociation proceeds linearly from that altitude to completion at 140 miles (220 km.). This may be an incorrect assumption because the ionized nitrogen molecule (N_2^+) has been detected in all auroral spectra, that is, up to a height of 700 miles (1,100 km.).[22]

The Rocket Panel data assume that the average molecular weight

* *h* is Planck's constant, $6{\cdot}62 \times 10^{-27}$ erg. sec; *v* is the frequency of the radiation. For example the Hartley continuum gives values of *h.v* varying from $6{\cdot}12 \times 10^{-12}$ erg to $9{\cdot}65 \times 10^{-12}$ erg, or 3·84 to 6·0 electron volts.

of the atmospheric constituents is constant at 28·9 (N_2 and O_2) up to 50 miles (80 km.), then changes linearly with altitude to 23·4 (N_2 and O) at 75 miles (120 km.) and then again linearly with increasing altitude, reaching 14·5 (N and O) at 140 miles (220 km.). These figures differ from those employed in the Rand Report by Grimminger,[13] where the presence of molecular nitrogen was assumed up into the 250-mile (400 km.) level, and which does appear to be borne out by the auroral spectroscopic studies. It is perhaps important in correlating Rocket Panel data with photo-chemical theory, that rocket data measurements indicate a mean molecular weight which is too high for the photo-chemical results. This may be because the effects of ionization cannot yet be allowed for. Ionization reduces the average molecular weight because there are present in the gas both free electrons and ions. For example, completely ionized oxygen, that is with all atoms ionized, would have a mean molecular weight of only 8 because there would be as many electrons as ions.

It may be that these problems will not be completely solved until a rocket can be sent into the upper regions of the atmosphere carrying as its instrumentation a device which will be able to differentiate between molecular and atomic nitrogen. A possibility of this being done lies with the radio-frequency mass spectrograph (Fig. 4.10) developed by Townsend[23] of the Naval Research Laboratory. This instrument should be able to measure the ratio of N/N_2 and currently it has been employed in V-2 and Aerobee rockets to check if diffusive separation of the atmospheric gases is taking place.

Two Aerobee rockets, launched in April 1954, carried four-stage radio-frequency mass spectrometers having increased resolution and new gas inlet systems and break-off devices. These were used to check the dissociation of O_2 and should give useful information when the data is evaluated. Viking rocket No. 10, launched on 7th May, 1954 to a peak of 136 miles (220 km.), carried a mass spectrometer for measuring ion composition and relative abundances in the E and F regions.

If the Earth's atmosphere were undisturbed and no mixing processes were at work, it would, over the passage of time, attain isothermal equilibrium. The various gases would settle in layerlike form with the lightest ones at the top and the heaviest closest to the Earth's surface. In the troposphere and stratosphere such gravitational separation is prevented by turbulent mixing processes, but above 150

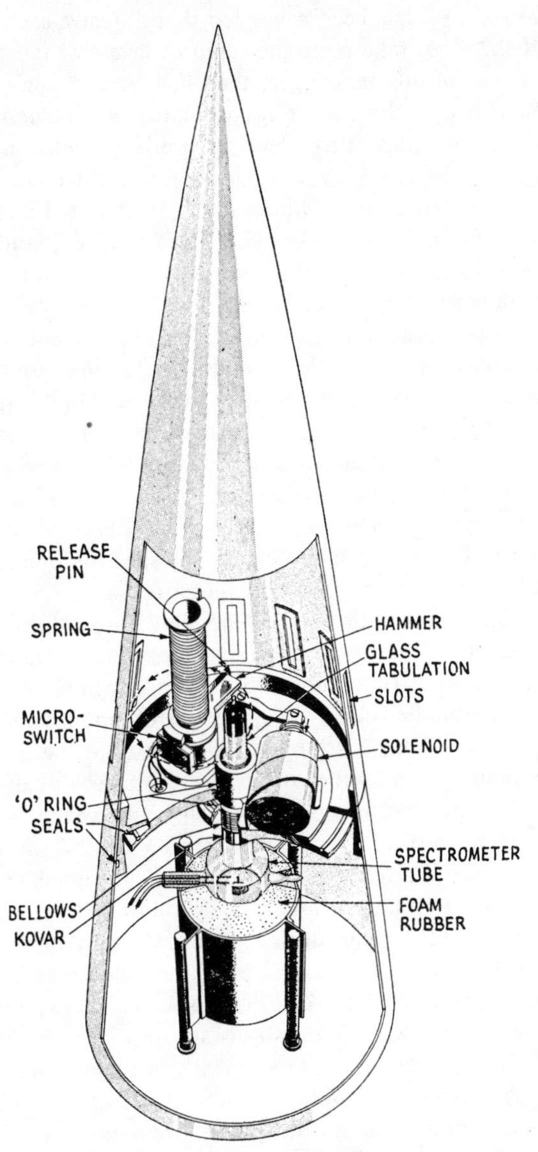

FIG. 4.10—A drawing of Aerobee NRL–13 showing the spectrometer inlet, the breaker and the slotted section of the conical nose fairing.

(Official United States Navy photograph)

miles (240 km.) it has been suggested that diffusive separation may occur. If this does take place the topmost layers of the atmosphere would consist of atomic oxygen, then helium and finally hydrogen at the outer fringe. But this brings a number of problems.

The decay of radio-active elements produces radon and helium. Radon is an inert heavy gas (atomic weight 222) which sinks to the bottom of the atmosphere where it can be detected in the air. On the other hand, helium should exist in reasonable quantities in the atmosphere for it, too, is inert. Moreover, in addition to being produced by the disintegration of radium it is also evolved in most radio-active decay processes. It is released into the atmosphere, for example, by natural gases from petroleum wells. These many sources should give a greater percentage of helium than is found in the atmosphere, namely 0·0005 per cent by volume. Because it is a light gas it may be expected that it has risen to the top of the atmosphere and that all the helium released since earliest geological times should be represented by an outer atmospheric layer. In fact it is found that no such outer fringe of helium can be detected by spectroscopic analysis of the light from the aurorae and the night airglow.

One possible explanation is that the high temperature of the exosphere is sufficient to give the helium atoms enough kinetic energy for them to escape. These atoms in the fringe regions would accordingly reach parabolic velocity and leak off into interplanetary space, never to return. If this is so, hydrogen, which has higher molecular velocities than helium for the same temperature because of its smaller molecular weight, can escape more easily and should accordingly not be detected either. There is a check on this which appears to confirm the theory. If hydrogen were present in the upper atmosphere, Bates has shown[24] that the hydrides, NH and OH, would form by photo-chemical action. As these resonate strongly in sunlight and emit bands close to 3,360A and 3,090A, they should easily be detected in the spectrum of the twilight atmosphere. These bands are not detected. However, Meinel[25] has now shown that there are definite bands of OH between 7,000A and 9,000A in the infra-red spectrum of the night airglow. Hydrogen does, therefore, appear to be present in the upper atmosphere but the quantity remains in doubt and the mystery of the disappearing helium still rests unsolved.

Attempts to ascertain if diffusive separation is occurring have accordingly been made by rocket-borne instruments. They have taken two forms, a sampling-bottle technique used by the University of Michigan[26] in conjunction with analysis by the University of Durham[27] and the use of radio-frequency mass spectrometers by the Applied Physics Laboratory of the Johns Hopkins University[28] and by the Naval Research Laboratory.[23]

In the early sampling techniques using V-2 rockets, the sampling bottles were placed in the mid and tail sections. This was done in order to ensure safe recovery after the flight with minimum damage to the bottles on impact. The first flight took place in 1947 using V-2 number 30 launched at 5.55 a.m. on 29th July, which attained a peak altitude of 99 miles (159 km.). The samples from these steel bottles were pumped into glass storage tanks on recovery and the glass may have contaminated the gases. In addition, leaks from the rocket itself may have produced contamination, so although no diffusive separation was detected at heights of up to 44 miles (70 km.), these results could not be regarded as conclusive.

However, over a period of years, the sampling technique and the sampling bottles were improved. Installations were flown in Aerobee rockets in 1949 reaching peaks between 31 miles (50 km.) and 37·5 miles (60 km.) and earlier tests were made in V-2 rockets in 1947 and 1948. One more modern design was mounted at the most forward part of the Aerobee rockets SC17 and 21 fired to peaks of 51 miles (82 km.) on 19th December, 1950, and 43 miles (69 km.) on 26th February, 1951, respectively. A nose cone was blown off by a solid-propellent rocket unit in order to clear all structure forward of the intake ports and thus avoid contamination from gases carried up in the structure of the rocket. The sampling bottles were mounted in groups of three and were recovered by parachute. A similar instrumentation was mounted in V-2 number 59 fired to a peak altitude of 78 miles (124 km.) on 20th May, 1952. In this case two lots of three sampling bottles were mounted at the nose tip and recovered separately by parachute. Oxygen is not measured in the tests because it disappeared readily during storage in the steel bottles and also it oxidizes the copper inlet tubes. The gases chosen for the analysis were therefore the inert ones, namely one of medium weight, nitrogen, a light gas, helium, and a heavy gas, argon.

Analyses have indicated the operation of diffusive separation at the greatest altitudes reached,[29] but some doubt is cast on the validity of the results because separation was also found in control samples.[30]

The alternative method for testing for diffusive separation is that of using a radio-frequency mass spectrometer. In this instrument (Fig. 4.11) the gas molecules are ionized and the charged ions then accelerated by a magnetic field which is alternated at radio frequencies. The result is that the molecules arrange themselves accord-

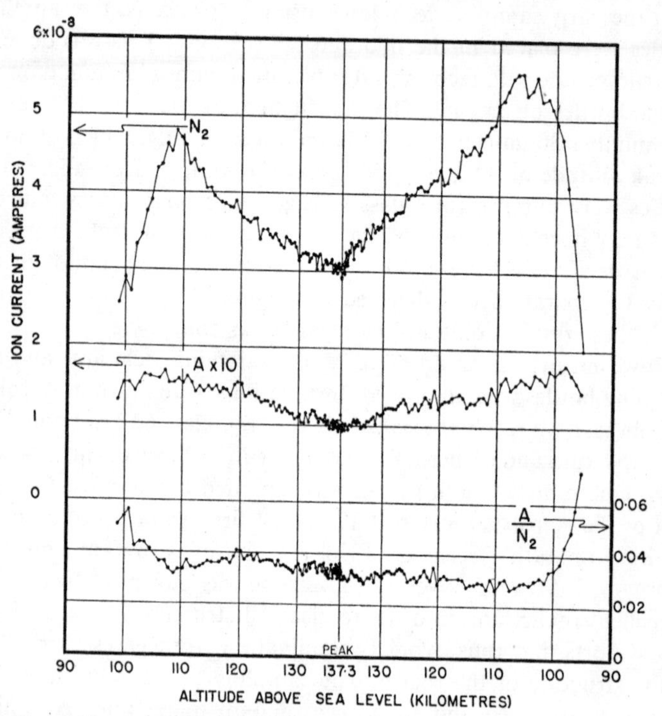

FIG. 4.14—A graph of the results from Aerobee NRL–13, ion currents for argon, molecular nitrogen and ratio A/N_2 plotted against altitude. The ratio A/N_2 decreases with altitude thereby suggesting that diffusive separation is not taking place.

(*Courtesy, Naval Research Laboratory*)

ing to their molecular weight, thus enabling the atmospheric constituents to be recognized.

The Applied Physics Laboratory of Johns Hopkins University flew a mass spectrometer in Aerobee A18, 17th August, 1950, and Aerobee A19, 22nd January, 1951, but unfortunately the equipment failed and no data were obtained.[28] Another spectrometer by the Naval Research Laboratory[23] was flown in a Viking rocket and a

FIG. 4.11 (*left*)—The radiofrequency mass spectrometer tube used in Aerobee NRL-13 to test for diffusive separation of the upper-atmospheric gases.

(*Official United States Navy photograph*

FIG. 4.12 (*below*)—The complete nose cone of Aerobee NRL-13 instrumented for testing diffusive separation.

(*Official United States Navy photograph*

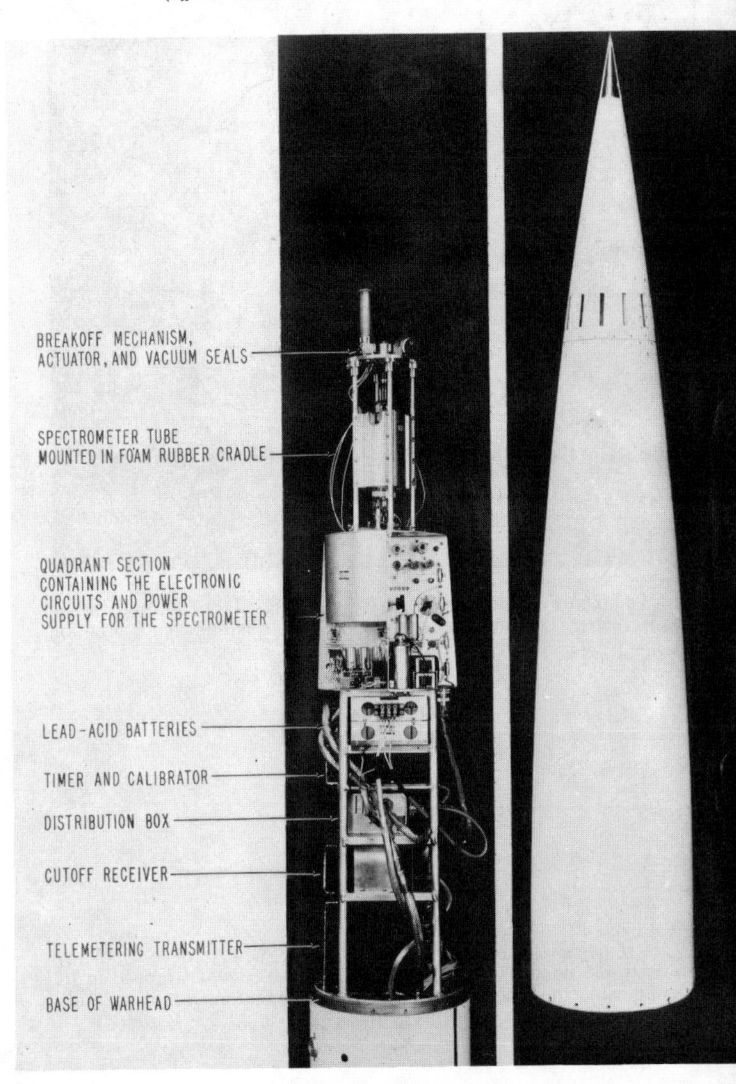

'acing p. 68]

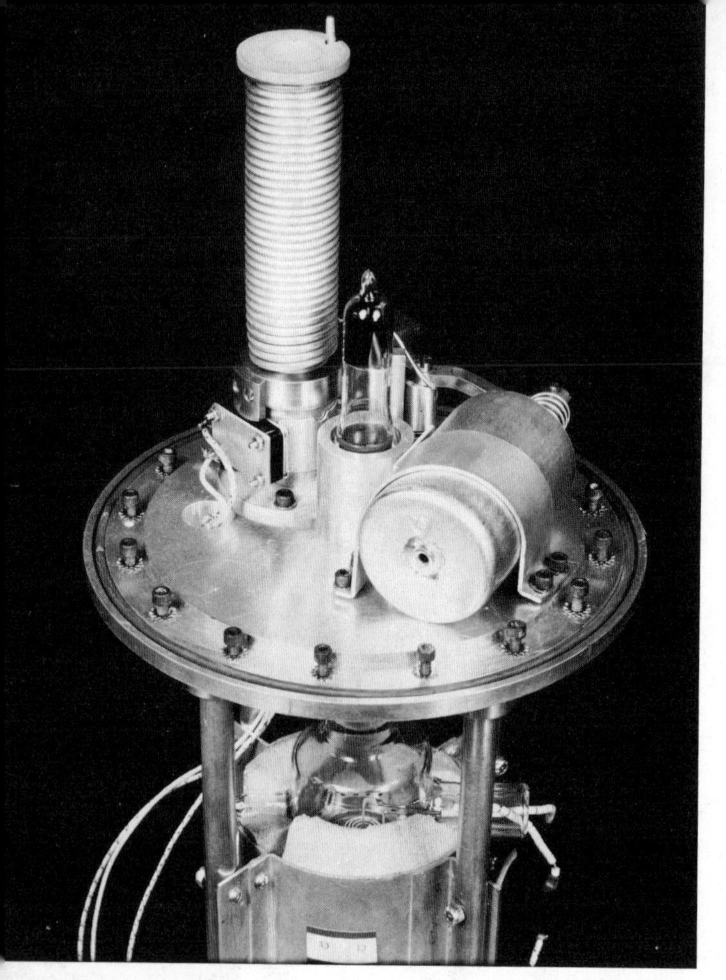

FIG. 4.13 (*above*)—The mechanism for breaking off the tube of the mass spectrometer when the atmospheric pressure was sufficiently low for the spectrometer to operate effectively.

(*Official United States Navy photograph*

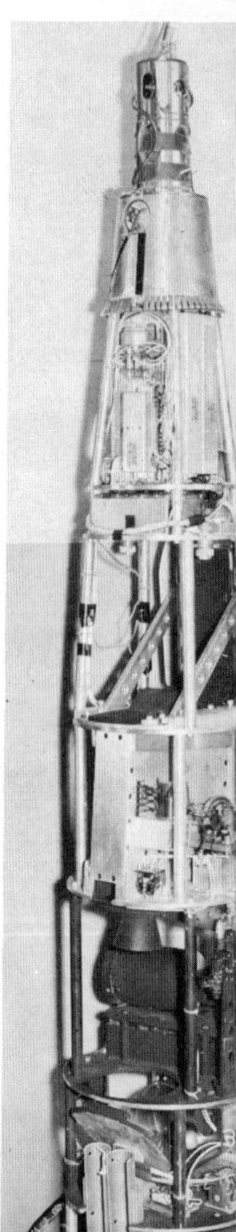

FIG. 4.16 (*right*)—The nose cone of the Aero-med Aerobee. Half-way down is the compartment in which the monkey was strapped in its harness, while the chamber for the mice is at the bottom of the 'warhead'.

(*Official United States Air Force photograph*

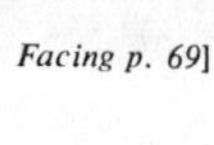

Facing p. 69]

V-2 rocket during 1952 but these experiments also were not successful. Accordingly two Aerobee rockets were instrumented and flown in 1953. The first, NRL–12, was fired at 2.9 p.m. on the 10th February and the second, NRL–13, was fired at nine minutes past midnight on 12th February. These were specially lightened rockets and both reached a peak of 85 miles (137 km.). The mounting of the instrumentation is shown in Figs. 4.10 and 4.12, and details of the breaker mechanism for the glass seal of the spectrograph are shown in Fig. 4.13. Data were telemetered to the ground station. Unfortunately, no worthwhile results were obtained with the flight of NRL–12, but NRL–13 gave some interesting and useful data. The results have indicated that there is no diffusive separation up to the peak altitude reached. This was concluded from comparison of the ratio of argon to molecular nitrogen (Fig. 4.14). From these curves it can be seen that the ratio A/N_2 decreased with altitude whereas the effect of diffusive separation would be to reverse this tendency and increase the ratio at high altitudes. It is now thought, from most recent data, that there is no diffusive separation of the atmospheric gases below 100 miles (160 km.).

One important phenomenon has been recognized from upper-atmosphere work and that is the presence of high-velocity winds in the ionosphere.[31] These winds have been suspected for some time because of undulations and drifts of noctilucent clouds and the motions of persistent meteor trails. During the past few years radio astronomy and rockets have both yielded data on these high-altitude wind systems. Radio astronomers have observed the scintillations of radio sources during the passage of the radio waves from the radio star to the ground-based observers. Several stations, separated by suitable distances, have compared plots of these scintillations and have recognized patterns which were repeated at one station a few minutes after they had been observed at a distant station. From these observations it has been inferred that ionospheric peculiarities are in horizontal motion, but there was some doubt as to whether or not such phenomena could be explained as winds or merely as wave motions within the ionized layers.

It is now generally accepted that there are definite drifts of irregularities in the ionosphere which can be regarded as winds. A number of observations over a period of years made at the Jodrell Bank experimental station of the University of Manchester, at Cambridge, at the Radio Research Station at Slough, and in other countries, has enabled these winds to be classified. In the mid-northern latitudes it has been found that in summer the winds are always easterly and may reach speeds of 205 miles per hour (100 metres/sec.). In the winter the winds are westerly during the morning but easterly at other times. It appears too that magnetic activity produced by solar

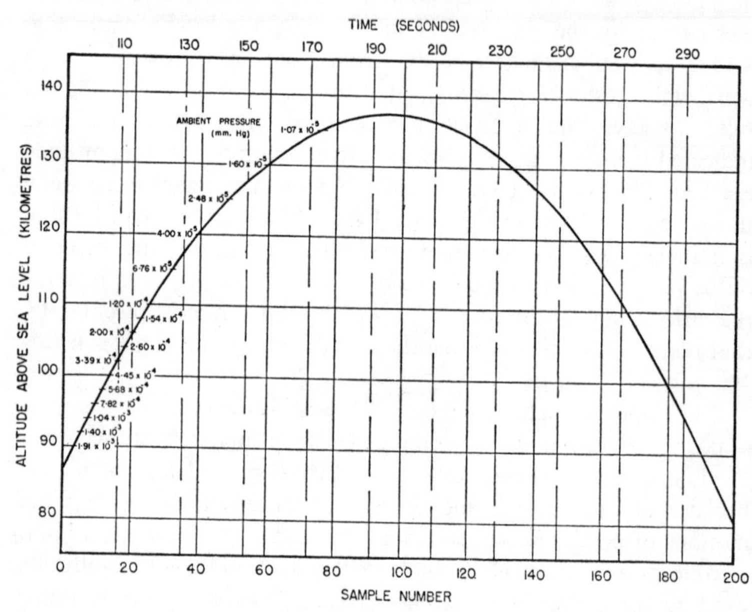

FIG. 4.15—The flight of Aerobee NRL–13 showing altitude and pressures against time from launching and also the sampling number for the diffusive separation experiment.

(Courtesy, Naval Research Laboratory)

storms has an effect upon the wind system, producing increased wind velocities. The ionized layer winds flow at altitudes of between 50 miles (80 km.) and 190 miles (300 km.) and more detailed work is needed to ascertain the vertical components.

These radio results have been confirmed by rocket experiments made by Ference[32] of the University of Michigan. Six Aerobees were instrumented during 1950 and 1951 and fired during the night-time. In each of these rockets there were seven, short, cannon-like barrels containing grenades which could be ejected at predetermined intervals by small propelling charges. A timing fuse ensured that the grenades would explode when they were approximately 200 feet (60 metres) from the rocket. The flash of the explosion was photographed by ground-based cameras and triangulation gave the altitude. In addition, photocells in the rocket itself telemetered the time of the flash.

The sound of the explosion was detected by an array of microphones arranged in a L-shape on the ground beneath the rocket. From the times of arrival of the sound of the explosions at each microphone it was possible to calculate the speeds and directions of the winds. Again it was found that during the summer the winds were easterlies changing to westerlies in the winter. This, however, differs from the radio work in so far as the latter showed easterlies during the night when the rocket measurements were taken. The summer westerlies were found to have a speed of about 210 miles per hour (104 metres/sec.) maximum at an altitude of between 30 and 37 miles (50–60 km.). On the other hand the easterlies had top speeds of only 185 miles per hour (90 metres/sec.). From this work, too, air temperatures were computed and these were found to be in good agreement with other rocket results.

In connexion with the high-altitude winds, meteor trail photography has shown that these winds may vary greatly in speed over the height range traced out by the meteor's path, and, moreover, the winds were sometimes found to reverse in direction over the range of altitudes covered by the meteor.

The energy for the production of these winds in the upper regions of the atmosphere undoubtedly comes from the Sun in the form of radiation. Variable conditions may hence be produced when the Earth is subjected to unusual radiation such as intense ultra-violet or X-rays, or even the corpuscular streams which produce the aurorae. Tidal effects may additionally give rise to upper-air drifts. We see, therefore, that the upper atmosphere is no quiescent region, as was at one time believed, but that it acts as a buffer to the conditions and radiations in space. Moreover, in addition to providing earthly life with gases for its sustenance it blankets such life from harmful radiations which would otherwise quickly sterilize the planet.

There is a good deal of discussion nowadays regarding the possibilities of manned space flight. Technically there would appear to be strong chances that man will have machines capable of carrying him into space by the end of the present century. A great amount of technical and engineering practice has to be obtained before man's interplanetary aspirations can become more than dreams, but at the present rate of progress it is not being unduly optimistic to prophesy that the necessary experience in the building, handling, and control of rockets sufficiently large in size will have been gained within the next fifty years.

Although machines may thus be constructed capable of journeying into space, man himself may undergo unpleasant reactions once he is removed from the protection of the terrestrial atmosphere. Human beings are such delicately balanced living organisms that they often find even the whirl of modern civilized city life both mentally and physically trying. Will man, himself, therefore, be the weak link in the chain of events leading to interplanetary flight? Lift unprotected man fifty miles upwards and he would die. Of that there is no doubt!

At three miles or so difficulties are encountered with respiration. Oxygen has to be supplied artificially to make up for the reduced percentage of this gas in the alveolar air. At ten miles no oxygen at all can be taken into the lungs from the atmosphere and the contribution to respiration becomes nil. At about this height, too, difficulties are encountered with the low pressure causing the body fluids to boil. First the saliva foams around the mouth, then the fluid on the eyeballs, ultimately blisters form under the skin. These vesicles are thought to be due to the formation of bubbles of water vapour in the soft tissues. These effects are pronounced when the pressure of the atmosphere falls to about 47 mm. Hg because that is the water vapour pressure at normal bodily temperature. At greater heights still the blood would begin to foam in the lungs.

It is fairly easy to protect man from these hazards by means of a pressurized cabin. This matter has already been tackled by the aeronautical world because planes like the Douglas Skyrocket have ascended to altitudes of 15 miles (24 km.). But, of course, this solution brings in its wake a further problem; the fate of the human beings should the pressure fail, for example, by an accident or an enemy bullet. It would appear from experiments with explosive decompression that there is very little chance of survival unprotected in the above emergency. While at an altitude of 30,000 feet (10,000 metres) the time of useful consciousness from normal atmosphere to sudden exposure to conditions at that altitude, amounts to about two minutes, at 50,000 feet (16,500 metres) the period is only fifteen seconds. Any escape from a failing high-altitude craft must, therefore, be made in some capsule or pressure suit and this type of garment is, hence, now being produced.

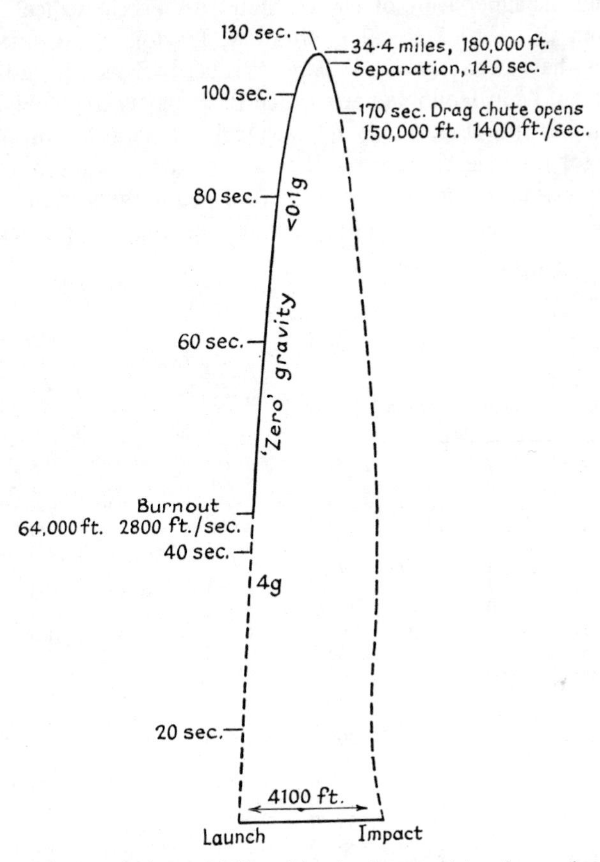

FIG. 4.17—Trajectory followed by the Aero-med Aerobee rocket showing the period when the rocket was in free fall and the animals experienced zero gravity.

(Courtesy, United States Air Force)

Then, of course, higher in the atmosphere there are hazards due to intense ultra-violet radiation and the cosmic-ray primaries, while from the time of all-burnt of a freely moving rocket vehicle any occupants can become weightless. These types of problems are becoming ever more important as rocket planes creep higher and higher into the realms of the upper atmosphere and consequently a new science of space-medicine is developing from that of aero-medicine.

Under the supervision of United States Air Force medical scientists from the Aero Medical Laboratory, Dayton, Ohio, mice and monkeys have been flown in V-2 and Aerobee rockets. The tests were carried out from Holloman Air Force Base and White Sands.

In the Aerobee (Fig. 4.16, p. 69) the medical laboratory consisted of spaces for an anaesthetized monkey and a pair of white mice. The monkey was cushioned in a specially designed harness and reactions such as heart rate, respiration, venous and arterial pressure were

TABLE 4.3 *Rocket Panel Atmospheric Data*

Height above sea level miles	*km.*	*Temp. °K.* (μ = 28·966)	*Adopted mol. wt. g/mol.* (μ)	*Temp. °K.* (μ varies)	*Pressure* $\log_{10}$ *dyn/cm*^{2}	*Density* $\log_{10}$ *g/cm*^{3}	*Mean free path cm.*
·75	1·216	291·0	28·97	291·0	5·945	−2·977	8·6 × 10^{-6}
6·21	10	230·8	28·97	230·8	5·446	−3·375	2·1 × 10^{-5}
12·4	20	212·8	28·97	212·8	4·755	−4·030	9·7 × 10^{-5}
18·6	30	231·7	28·97	231·7	4·095	−4·728	4·8 × 10^{-4}
24·8	40	262·5	28·97	262·5	3·497	−5·380	2·2 × 10^{-3}
31.1	50	270·8	28·97	270·8	2·955	−5·936	7·8 × 10^{-3}
37·3	60	252·8	28·97	252·8	2·404	−6·457	2·6 × 10^{-2}
43·5	70	218·0	28·97	218·0	1·784	−7·012	9·3 × 10^{-2}
49·7	80	205·0	28·97	205·0	1·094	−7·676	4·3 × 10^{-1}
56·0	90	217·0	27·52	206·2	0·405	−8·389	2·1 × 10^{0}
62·1	100	240·0	26·22	217·3	−0·227	−9·065	9·5 × 10^{0}
68·5	110	270·0	25·03	233·3	−0·794	−9·684	3·8 × 10^{1}
74·6	120	330·0	23·95	272·8	−1·273	−10·249	1·3 × 10^{2}
80·9	130	390·0	22·50	302·9	−1·670	−10·720	3·7 × 10^{2}
87·0	140	447·0	21·21	327·3	−2·009	−11·119	8·7 × 10^{2}
93·2	150	503·0	20·06	348·4	−2·308	−11·468	1·8 × 10^{3}
99·4	160	560·0	19·34	368·0	−2·574	−11·781	3·6 × 10^{3}
105·5	170	618·7	18·10	386·7	−2·813	−12·062	6·1 × 10^{3}
112·0	180	676·9	17·26	403·4	−3·030	−12·318	1·0 × 10^{4}
118·0	190	734·9	16·50	418·5	−3·228	−12·552	1·8 × 10^{4}
124·0	200	792·5	15·79	432·1	−3·411	−12·768	3·0 × 10^{4}
130·5	210	849·8	15·15	444·4	−3·580	−12·968	5·1 × 10^{4}
147·0	220	906·6	14·55	455·5	−3·738	−13·154	8·7 × 10^{4}

The data are based on results of experiments by the following agencies: Naval Research Laboratory (R. Havens, R. Koll and H. Lagow); Signal Corps Electronic Laboratory, U.S. Army (M. Ference), University of Michigan, Air Force (H. S. Sicinski, N. W. Spencer, and W. G. Dow); University of Michigan, Signal Corps. They are reproduced by permission of Dr. F. L. Whipple, of the Rocket Panel, and the Editor, *The Physical Review*, Ref. 9.

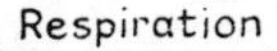

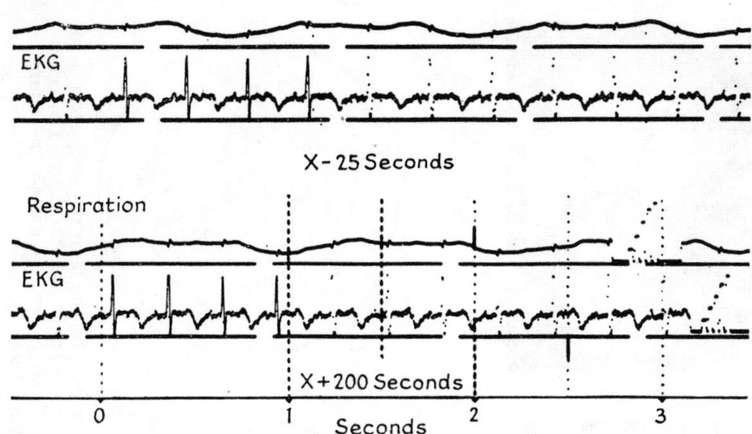

FIG. 4.18—Telemetered record of the respiration and heartbeats of the monkey showing that they did not differ greatly after a period of 200 seconds, that is during the fall to Earth by parachute.

(Courtesy, United States Air Force)

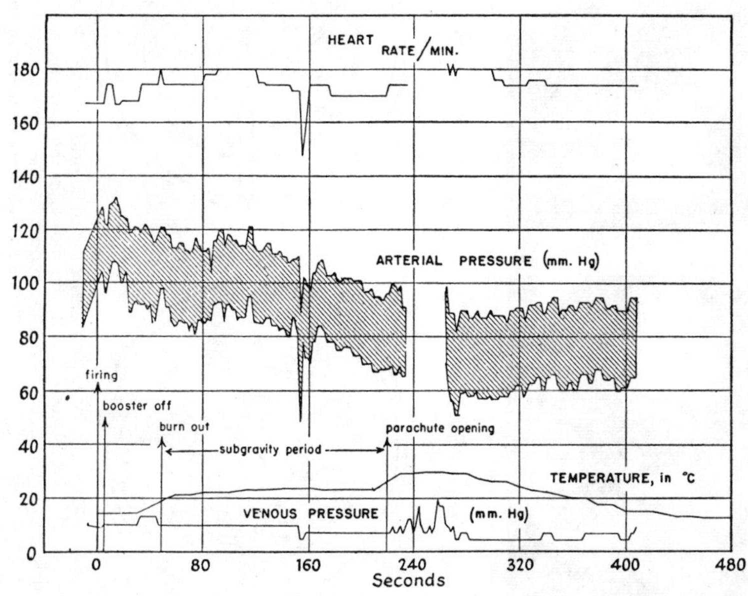

FIG. 4.19—Telemetered record of heart rate, arterial and venous pressures, and temperature, against time of flight. The various stages are shown such as booster operating, free fall conditions and parachute opening.

(Courtesy, United States Air Force)

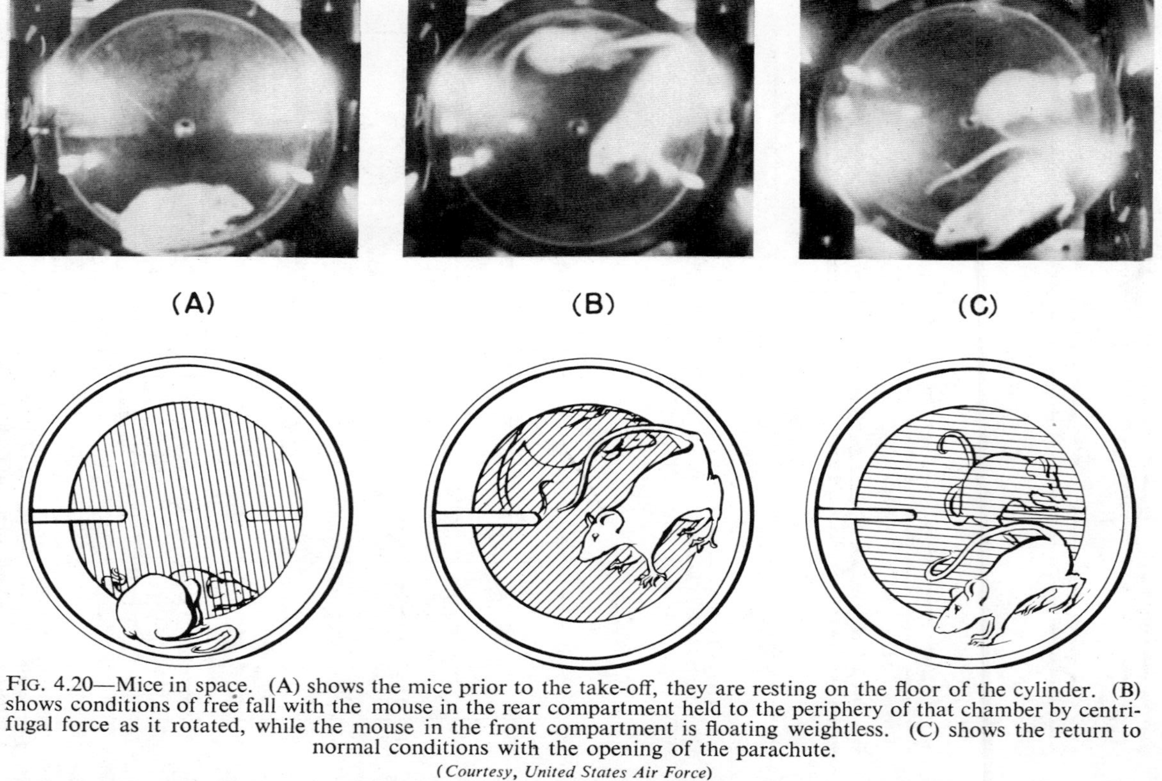

FIG. 4.20—Mice in space. (A) shows the mice prior to the take-off, they are resting on the floor of the cylinder. (B) shows conditions of free fall with the mouse in the rear compartment held to the periphery of that chamber by centrifugal force as it rotated, while the mouse in the front compartment is floating weightless. (C) shows the return to normal conditions with the opening of the parachute.

(Courtesy, United States Air Force)

telemetered (Fig. 4.18 and 4.19). The mice were free to move about in two compartments. The mouse at the rear had a shelf on to which it could climb, while the other mouse had a small ball in its compartment.

The trajectory of the Aerobee rocket is shown in Fig. 4.17. At take-off an acceleration of 14 g. was experienced as the rocket speeded up to the all-burnt velocity of 2,000 miles per hour (3,200 km./hr.). During this period the mice are both at the bottom of their containers. Then in free fall they float free, the one at the rear finding it advantageous to cling to its shelf. When the parachute opens they both fall to the floor again.

The monkey survived without ill effects, and it can be seen from Fig. 4.18 that there were no unusual effects in the various telemetered readings. The mice also survived and are being bred to test if any effects occur in subsequent generations due to primary cosmic rays.

The outcome of this biological work is that it has been concluded that mammals can function within the range of normalcy during rocket flights of this nature. However, many more tests will undoubtedly have to be made before man himself travels outwards to beyond the appreciable atmosphere.

REFERENCES

[1] Gowan, E. H., *Jnl. Roy. Met. Soc. Suppl.*, **62**, 34, 1936

[2] Wilkes, M. V., *Oscillations of the Earth's Atmosphere*, Cambridge Monographs, 1949

[3] Whipple, F. J. W., *Ger. Beitr. z Geophys.*, **24**, 72, 1929

[4] Whipple, F. L., *Rev. Modern Physics*, **15**, 246, 1943

[5] Vegard, L., Tönsberg, E., *Geofys. Publ.* (Oslo), **16**, No. 2, 1944

[6] Appleton, E. V., *Proc. Royal Soc. A*, **162**, 451, 1937

[7] Penndorf, R., *Bull. Americ. Met. Soc.*, **27**, 331, 1946

[8] Godfrey, G. H., Price, W. L., *Proc. Royal Soc. A*, **163**, 228, 1937

[9] The Rocket Panel, *Physical Review*, **88**, 1027, 1952

[10] Petrie, W., *Physical Review*, **88**, 790, 1952

[11] Friedman, H., Lichtman, S. W., Byram, E. T., *Physical Review*, **83**, 1025, 1951

[12] Spitzer, L., Jr., *Astrophysical Journal*, **95**, 329, 1942

[13] Grimminger, G., Analysis of Temperature, Pressure and Density of the Atmosphere Extending to Extreme Altitudes, *Rand Corporation Report*, 1948

[14] *Naval Research Laboratory Report* R-2955, Upper Atmosphere Report No. 1, October, 1946

[15] *Naval Research Laboratory Report* R-3030, Upper Atmosphere Report No. 2, December, 1946

[16] SCHULTZ, F. V., SPENCER, N. W., REIFMAN, A., *University of Michigan, Upper Air Research Programme*, Report No. 2, 1948
[17] HAVENS, R., KOLL, R., LAGOW, H., *Review of Scientific Instr.*, **21**, 596, 1950
[18] PANETH, F. A., *Quart. Jnl. Roy. Met. Soc.*, **63**, 433, 1937
[19] BATES, D. R., WITHERSPOON, A. E., *Monthly Notices, Roy. Astron. Soc.*, **109**, 215, 1949
[20] PILLOW, M. E., *Proc. Physical Society, A*, **66**, 1064, 1953
[21] JOHNSON, F. S., *Bull. Americ. Met. Soc.*, **34**, 106, 1953
[22] BATES, D. R., *Monthly Notices, Roy. Astron. Soc.*, **109**, 215, 1949
[23] TOWNSEND, J. W. JR., *Review of Scientific Instr.*, **23**, 538, 1952
[24] BATES, D. R., *loc. cit.*, 22
[25] MEINEL, A. B., Reports on the Progress of Physics, *The Physical Society, XIV*, 121, 1951
[26] LOH, L., NEILL, H., NICHOLS, M., WENZEL, E., *Review of Scientific Instr.*, **23**, 339, 1952
[27] PANETH, F. A., *Endeavour, XII*, 5, 1953
[28] FRAZER, L. W., Johns Hopkins University, *Bumblebee Report*, 153, 1951
[29] CHACKETT, K. F., PANETH, F. A., WILSON, E. J., *Nature*, **164**, 317, 1952
[30] *University of Michigan Report*, *Measurement of Diffusive Separation in the Upper Atmosphere*, Oxford Conference, Gassiot Committee, 1953
[31] *The Observatory*, **71**, 104, 1951
[32] FERENCE, M. J., *Transac. American Geophys. Union*, 317, 1952

Chapter Five

THE IONOSPHERE

⋙ ⦀ ⋘

IN earlier chapters we have seen that above the stratosphere is the part of the atmosphere known as the ionosphere. This is a region in which radiation and particles, principally emanating from the Sun, enter the rarefied atmosphere, interact with the atmospheric gases, exchange energies and ionize the atoms and the molecules. Although nearly all the gases in the ionosphere are thus affected, the ionization becomes most apparent in fairly definite layers. In addition, the growth and the decay of the ionized atoms and molecules causes a glow to be emitted which appears as the day and night airglows and, under certain circumstances, as the aurorae: the northern and southern lights. Moreover, sheets of electric current which affect the magnetic field of the Earth are set up in the ionized layers.

The principal layers of ionization occurring in the atmosphere are known as the D, E, and F layers, and these have, in fact, been recognized for some time, having been located by the measurements associated with radio propagation. In effect, a radio wave entering the ionosphere can be refracted in such a way that the wave is turned completely and the refraction appears as a reflection, the wave being returned to the Earth's surface by the ionized layer. This effect is shown in Fig. 2.2. The higher the degree of ionization the greater is the reflecting power of the layer and because the ionization is greater at lower atmospheric pressures, the upper layers become the best 'reflectors'. In addition the 'reflection' depends upon the frequency of the radiation hitting the layer, lower frequencies being more easily bent and sent back again. It also depends upon the angle at which the radiation strikes the ionospheric layer.

When a radio wave reaches the ionosphere, providing the angle made with the layer is sufficiently small, the wave will be deflected and returned to Earth. As the angle made with the layer is increased, the wave will be returned to the Earth's surface at a point nearer and nearer to the transmitter. If the angle is still further increased a limiting one will be reached at which the ionization is not sufficiently strong to bend the ray and allow its return. This angle is known as the critical angle; it varies, of course, with the frequency, and if this be raised, the critical angle will be reduced. Finally a limiting frequency can be obtained at which even with the smallest possible angle between the radiation and the layer, no 'reflection' would take place.

Conversely, if the frequency be reduced, the critical angle will increase, until this becomes a right angle. Then waves projected vertically upwards are returned. The frequency at which waves projected vertically change from being returned to penetrating the ionized layer, is known as the critical frequency for that layer. It is thus apparent that by choosing appropriate frequencies which are 'reflected' from the layers even when projected vertically, it is possible to measure the heights of the important ionized layers. A record is taken of the time which elapses between a pulse being transmitted and its returning to Earth after having been turned around by the layer. Knowing the speed at which the radiation travels it is possible thus to compute the height of the 'reflecting' layer. This is known as the virtual height (h) which is half the equivalent path (P'). It is somewhat greater than the actual height reached by the wave because the turning-round process within the layer takes a finite amount of time to be accomplished for there is not a true reflection as from a mirror-like surface.

By radio measurements based on these principles and notably by the pulse method developed by Breit and Tuve[1] a great amount of information has been accumulated concerning the layers. The method now employed is to transmit a series of radio frequency pulses, each of duration between 50 and 150 microseconds, to the ionosphere using a peak power in the region of several hundred watts. The frequency of the transmitter is varied over a range of frequencies at a controlled rate. The time taken for the pulses to return is an indication of the exploring or equivalent path (P') and this is plotted on a cathode-ray-tube screen against the transmitted frequency (f) producing what are known as P'-f curves (Figs. 5.1, 5.2) which are obtained by means of a moving film to give a permanent record. The various layers are shown quite well. From these P'-f curves it is

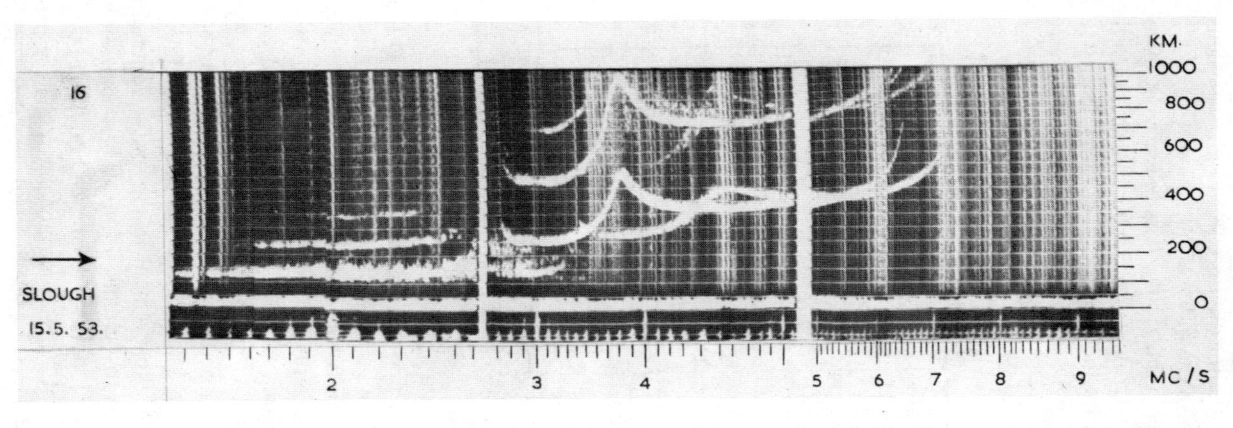

FIG. 5.1—A typical h'–f record obtained at the Radio Research Station, Slough, and reproduced by permission of the Director of Radio Research, Department of Scientific and Industrial Research. This shows clearly the E, F1 and F2 layers. Sometimes the vertical scale is calibrated as exploring path, P', instead of virtual height, h', as shown. The record then becomes known as a P'-f record (see text).

possible to calculate the maximum effective electron density in the ionizing region and also the index of refraction.

The inherent failing in the ground-based method is, of course, that it cannot be used to determine electron densities between the regions of maximum density in one layer and the same density in the next higher layer. This is one of the important reasons why rockets are needed for ionospheric work because instruments carried by them can make measurements in the ionosphere itself.

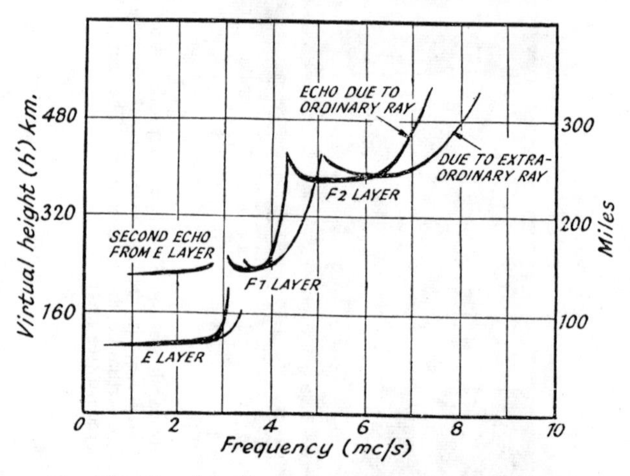

FIG. 5.2—Drawing of a h'–f record identifying the layers.

But the amount of data already assembled on these layers is quite impressive (Fig. 5.3). We know, for example, that the D layer, at a height of between 37 and 53 miles (60 and 85 km.), seems to arise from solar activity. This lowest ionized region is not normally recorded by the P'-f apparatus for it is essentially an absorbing rather than a 'reflecting' region, although it can be detected by low-frequency 'reflection', that is at frequencies below 30 kc/s. When the layer becomes highly ionized by conditions following a bright chromospheric eruption or a solar flare it causes a complete blanketing of short waves but an improvement in long-wave communication. The D layer is thought to be caused by the first ionization of the oxygen molecule or the ionization of the NO molecule, though the presence of NO has not been confirmed by rocket spectroscopic studies (see next chapter). It is nowadays thought, therefore, that the ionization of oxygen is the most likely mechanism, as D layer ionization is synchronous with the flash of ultra-violet light from the solar flares.

Attempts have been made with rockets to measure the collisional frequency in this region, but the data so far gathered has not yet been completely evaluated.[2]

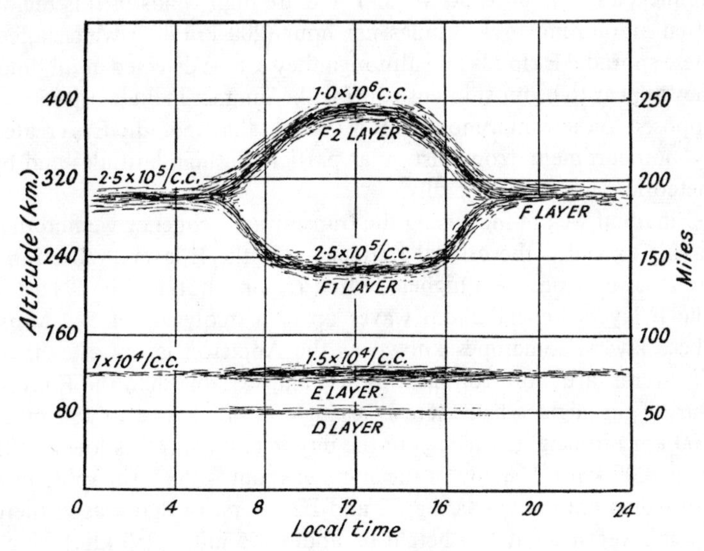

FIG. 5.3—The ionized layers of the Earth's atmosphere.

Between 62 miles and 75 miles (100 and 120 km.) is the most regular ionized region from which 'reflections' are normally obtained at frequencies below 3 Mc/s. This is the E layer, discovered independently by Kennelly and Heaviside and accordingly often known as the Kennelly-Heaviside layer. It has an effective maximum electron density which increases from minimum (1×10^4/cm.^{3}) just before dawn, reaches a maximum ($1{\cdot}5 \times 10^5$/cm.^{3}) at noon, then tails off to a minimum after sunset. It is least heavily ionized in the period from midnight to dawn. This layer can sometimes split into two, the E1 and E2 layers separated from each other by about 9 miles (15 km.), when the lower, E1, layer is found to reflect vertically projected radio signals up to a frequency of 2 Mc/s. The origin of the E layer, which has a sharp boundary when measured with the *P'-f* method, is not quite clear. It may be due to a pre-ionization process of molecular oxygen,[3] but the presence of a divided layer may indicate that two definite processes are separately responsible. X-radiation may be playing a great part in the creation of this layer.[4]

Overlapping the E layer is a region of sporadic E in which clouds of ionization sometimes permit long-distance communication with frequencies as high as 56 Mc/s. There are high winds in this region often amounting to 125 miles per hour (200 km./hr.) which affect these sporadic E clouds and although they can be detected at all times they appear to be most intense during the summer in high latitudes as opposed to the winter months. It is thought that sporadic E is created by bombardment from fast solar particles in high latitudes and by meteoric ionization generally.

Finally if we are increasing the transmitted frequency we find that having exceeded the critical frequency for the E layer, 'reflections' are received from even higher ionized regions, notably the F layers. The F layers 'reflect' radio waves up to a frequency of 5–8 Mc/s. These layers, sometimes known as the Appleton layers after their discoverer, are more complex, diffuse and variable than the E layer. During the night when there is a single layer, it rises to 190 miles (300 km.) in height, whereas in the daytime, it can be as low as 125 miles (200 km.). Usually in the summer months the layer splits into two which are known as the F1 and F2 layers. In that season there is one layer at night at a height of about 155 miles (250 km.) which splits into two at sunrise. The F1 layer is thought to be caused by the second ionization of molecular nitrogen or the first ionization of atomic oxygen, while the F2 layer has been postulated to be produced by the first ionization of molecular nitrogen, the first ionization of atomic oxygen or even the second and third ionizations of atomic oxygen. Bates and Massey[5] have suggested that the ionization of atomic oxygen could account for both the F1 and F2 layers.

Complex changes take place in the F layer at the time of storms on the Sun. It is found, in fact, that the state of ionization of the terrestrial atmosphere varies diurnally due to the rotation of the Earth, in a period of just over 27 days due to the rotation of the Sun, annually due to the revolution of the Earth around the Sun and also over a fairly long, eleven-year period, corresponding with the sunspot cycle. Indeed the Sun seems to play the most active part in controlling the state of the ionosphere. One important solar event which has complex effects, is the solar flare which Menzel has described[6] as arising when a funnel-type prominence breaks.

The flares occur near to sunspot groups and at sunspot maximum there may be four or five great flares during a year. The flare emits light very strongly at a wavelength of H_α and it may last for a period extending from several minutes to an hour. H_α is emitted when an electron passes from the M to L level in the possible electron orbits in a hydrogen atom. It is radiation in the visible red region of the spectrum at a wavelength of 6,562·8A. Usually there is an abrupt onset to the flare with a swift rise to maximum brilliance, followed by a gradual decline until the flare dies out completely. Intense ultra-violet light is emitted at the period of maximum brightness and this ultra-violet light, probably at the wavelength of H Lyman_α, reaches Earth within a few minutes of the actual occurrence. The Lyman series from Hydrogen was discovered by T. Lyman of Harvard University and it covers emission when electrons return from the various excited orbits directly to the lowest energy level, the K level. Lyman alpha is thus emitted when an electron moves from the L to the K level and it is at a wavelength of 1,275·7A. Lyman_β is at 1,026A. It is possible that the Lyman series is responsible for most of the upper-atmosphere ionization and Lyman_α is known to be able to penetrate both nitrogen and oxygen molecules in the Earth's atmosphere down to about 60 miles (100 km.) from the surface. This radiation affects the ionosphere, produces intense ionization in the D layer, giving wireless fade-out on short waves. In addition currents are generated in the upper layers producing what is known as a magnetic crochet, (Fig. 5.10), a sudden change in the Earth's magnetic field. This change may amount to as much as 100 gamma (where one gamma is equal to 10^{-5} gauss), in the horizontal component, H, of the Earth's field, 50 gamma in the vertical component, V, and as much as 5 minutes' deflection in the declination D. These effects only take place in the daylight hemisphere of the Earth, and the D region ionization also takes place in the daylight hemisphere. A flare often produces a burst of high-frequency radiation which appears on radio sets as 'solar noise'. But the flare also has secondary effects which are not apparent until some hours have elapsed. At the time of its occurrence, a stream of particles, thought to be electrically neutral, that is consisting of an equal number of protons and electrons, is emitted and travels as a conical spray across the 93,000,000 miles (150,000,000 km.) of space between the Sun and the Earth. These particles take about 27 hours to reach the vicinity of the Earth, travelling at an average speed of 1,000 miles per second (1,600 km./sec.). When they arrive they produce a magnetic storm, brilliant aurorae and interference with radio communication. These corpuscles produce effects which are felt in both the day and the night hemispheres, they disrupt the F layers, increase their height, reduce the electron density and the critical frequency and are even thought to set up ring currents around the Earth, a few Earth radii out in space.[7]

The aurora-producing mechanism has been deduced by Meinel[8] from spectroscopic examination of the light emitted by the great aurora of 18th–20th August, 1950. He found that the H_α line, λ6,563A, was broadened towards the ultra-violet so as to indicate a Doppler effect arising from protons approaching the Earth at a speed of 2,000 miles per second (3,200 km./sec.). This is, of course, much faster than the previously mentioned speed for the neutral corpuscular stream but there will doubtless be an accelerating effect from both the gravitational and magnetic fields of the Earth.

There is yet another type of magnetic storm produced by the Sun; it is known as the M-storm. This class of storm is very different from those associated with solar flares. There is an indefinite beginning, very little if any storm-time variation, the duration is fairly long and the storms tail off into indefinite endings. Usually they occur after a period of a solar rotation, that is, after 27·6 days and the emitting regions responsible were termed M regions by Bartels in 1934,[9] namely, magnetically effective regions. There is still a great deal of controversy concerning their origin and with which, if any, visible surface feature of the Sun they are associated. An unusually active sunspot, associated with radio emission (which normally takes place from the lower coronal regions in conjunction with sunspots) gave rise to magnetic M storms of a definite sequence.[10] It is also thought that coronal streams are sources of corpuscular beams which reach the Earth in a period of about one to three days[11, 12] and which may give rise to M storms.

The study of the ionosphere can thus conveniently be divided into two main sections; first, dealing with the ionized layers and their effects upon radio communication which depends a great deal upon the intensity of ionization and the heights of the layers. Then, secondly, it is important to consider the currents produced in the ionosphere and the effects which show as variations in the Earth's magnetic field.

From the data on rockets given in the earlier chapters it is at once apparent that high-altitude vehicles such as the Aerobee and the V-2, reaching peaks of 60–100 miles (100–160 km.) are entering the E regions while the Viking and the Bumper-WAC penetrate the F1 and F2 layers respectively. Ionospheric experiments made from the ground have been shown to be restricted in scope because they fail to provide information on ion and electron densities between the regions of maximum density in one ionospheric layer and the region of similar density in the next higher layer. The early V-2 experiments were, therefore, concerned with attempts to measure the ion density and the type of ions by transmitting near-critical frequencies from a multiplicity of aerials on the rocket and observing the results from fixed ground stations. In the high-altitude rocket programme first attempts were made to obtain direct measurements of the electron densities as a function of altitude together with the attenuation characteristics of the atmosphere also as a function of altitude. Later in the programme experiments were instrumented to study the effects of cross-modulation* in the ionosphere, to measure the collisional frequency and to check the propagation of radio waves over long distances both from ground stations to the ionosphere and from the rocket to ground stations.

The original experiments were undertaken by the United States Naval Research Laboratory in 1946,[13] by the instrumentation of a V-2 rocket in order to conduct a phase-beat experiment within the ionosphere (Fig. 5.4). Two harmonically related frequencies were transmitted from the rocket. The high frequency was chosen so that it would have an index of refraction of unity, hence its velocity of propagation would not be changed in passing through the ionized regions. On the other hand, the lower frequency, chosen to be just above the critical frequency for the day of the test, would have an index of refraction approaching zero, accordingly its velocity of propagation would be considerably changed. When passing through the ionized layers the lower frequency thus underwent a phase

* Cross-modulation, sometime known as the Luxembourg effect, is the impression of modulation from one carrier frequency upon another carrier frequency. It is caused by the radio carriers passing through the ionized layers where they experience absorptions and energy is transferred from one carrier to the other via the absorbing electrons.

retardation which could be detected at the ground station. This was accomplished by multiplying the frequency and mixing it with the high frequency. A phase beat was produced which could be displayed on a recording apparatus and made permanent by means of a cathode-ray tube and camera. The index of refraction could be computed

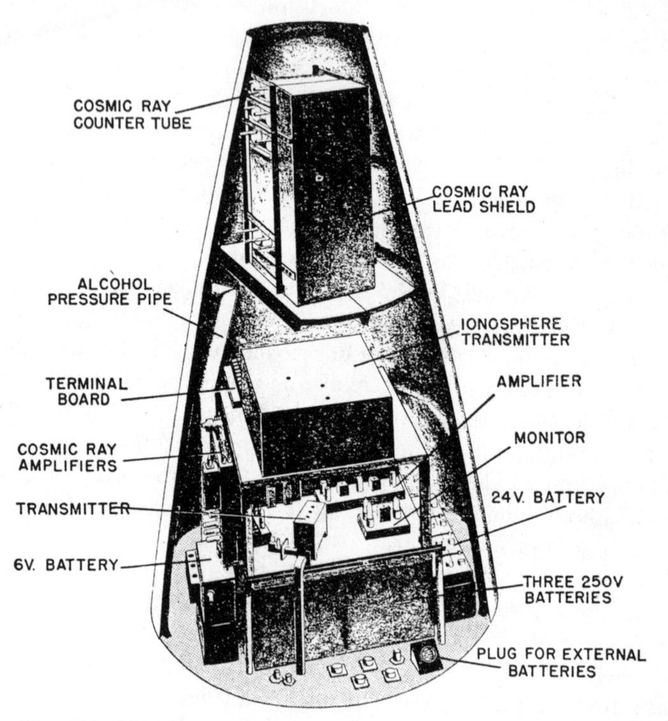

FIG. 5.4—V-2 warhead instrumentation showing the location of the ionosphere transmitter.
(*Courtesy, Naval Research Laboratory*)

from the phase beat and from that, in turn, it was possible to find the effective electron density.* It was calculated that the method was sensitive enough to record densities of less than 1,000 electrons per cubic centimetre. By keeping an accurate check on received signal strength it was also possible with this instrumentation to measure the attenuation effects of the layers at the two frequencies chosen.

Difficulties were encountered quite early as was to be expected.

* Assuming the ions to have the charge and mass of an electron.

First, the success of the experiments depended upon a phase beat; accordingly no spurious phase shifts could be tolerated anywhere in the apparatus. These were obviated by careful design of the receivers and transmitters. Then, of course, there was the problem associated with the designing of suitable aerial systems, especially for the lower frequency. The aerial had to have a good radiation pattern and, most important, remain attached to the rocket despite air drag and the action of the motor flame. Two types of aerials were used in the early experiments,[13] a trailing wire aerial and a delta aerial, the latter being suggested by Dr. M. H. Nichols of Princeton University.

The trailing wire aerials tried in the original experiment were of $\frac{3}{8}$-inch (9·5 cm.) twisted steel cable, suspended from the fins and unwound from special boxes as the rocket rose from the launching table. The deltas were constructed from copper-sheathed steel and stretched from the mid-section of the V-2 to the tail fins where they were attached by a spring-loaded attachment device (Fig. 3.3).

In the original experiment a crystal-controlled frequency of 334 kc/s. was used with its harmonics. The 48th harmonic, namely 25·632 Mc/s, was taken as the high-frequency reference signal, while a suitable low-frequency harmonic was chosen in relation to the critical frequency for the day of the launching determined from the P'-f apparatus. For example, the 12th harmonic, 6·408 Mc/s., is just above the critical frequency of the sporadic E region, while the 8th harmonic, 4·272 Mc/s., is slightly higher than the critical frequency of the normal E layer.

The first flight was in V-2 No. 5 launched at 4.40 p.m. on 13th June, 1946. This rocket reached an altitude of 73 miles (117 km.), but the aerials failed and the phase-beat experiment was not accomplished. Nevertheless it was found that with the delta aerials the input power of 6 watts at 12·8 Mc/s. (24th harmonic) gave a reasonable signal even from the peak of the trajectory. A number of subsequent flights were made to test instrumentations, the power was increased to 15 watts, and a flight of 30th July, 1946 (V-2 No. 9, peak altitude 104 miles [167 km.]), was successful except for transmitter trouble. Finally, 50 watts were used for the firing of 10th October, 1946, V-2 No. 12. Launching was at 10.15 a.m. and the rocket reached a peak of 102 miles (163 km.). This was a fairly successful flight even though the aerials did not survive. Essentially the flight tested the trailing-wire aerial system in which the aerials were each three-quarters of a wavelength in length, that is 7·92 metres for the reference frequency and 51·82 metres for the probe frequency of 4·272 Mc/s. Unfortunately the longer aerial caught at take-off and was pulled away from the rocket. The ionospheric phase-beat experiment was again frustrated but the higher reference frequency of 25·672 Mc/s. was received strongly even from the peak of the trajectory, and the ionized layers were found to have no appreciable effects on it. However, it

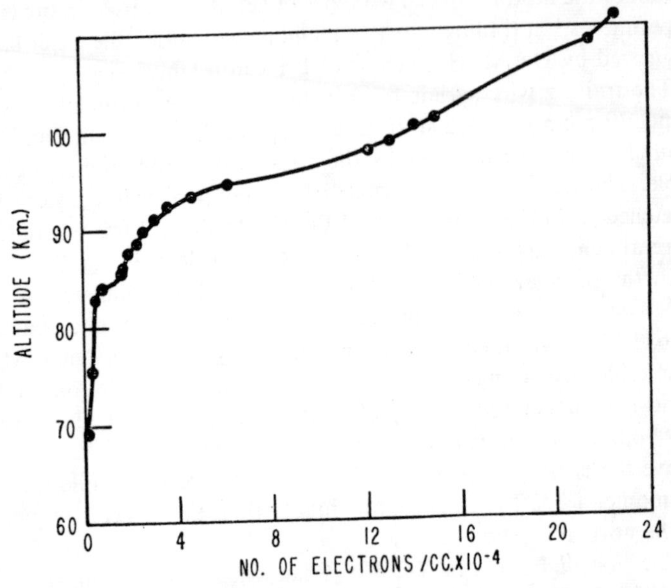

FIG. 5.5—Effective electron density against height obtained with a V-2 fired 7th March, 1947.

(Courtesy, Naval Research Laboratory and Pergamon Press)

was found that the radiation pattern was not good and the presence of many lobes, coupled with the rotation of the rocket after all-burnt, caused fluctuation of the received signal strength.[14]

Later flights were made with V-2 rockets in March 1947 (Fig. 5.5) and January 1948 (Fig. 5.6) in which results were obtained from the phase-beat experiment.[15, 16] On the flight of 7th March, 1947 (V-2 No. 21, launched 11.23 a.m., peak altitude 100 miles [160 km.]), the effective electron density below 83 km. was found to be 10^4/c.c., increasing to 2×10^5 at 69 miles (111 km.), where sporadic E ionization, which occurred just before take-off, effectively cut off the signals from the rocket transmitter. On the flight of 22nd January, 1948, (V-2 No. 34, launched 1.12 p.m., peak altitude 99 miles [158 km.]), again the electron density was less than 10^4/c.c. below 53 miles (85 km.), rising to $2{\cdot}3 \times 10^5$ at 60 miles (100 km.). Sporadic E once more interfered with the flight and blanketed the signals at 60 miles (100 km.). An interesting effect of the D layer was recorded on this flight arising from the attenuation programme. As the rocket rose through the region of the D layer there was a rapid fall in signal strength at 4·274 Mc/s. Moreover, during the descent the reverse

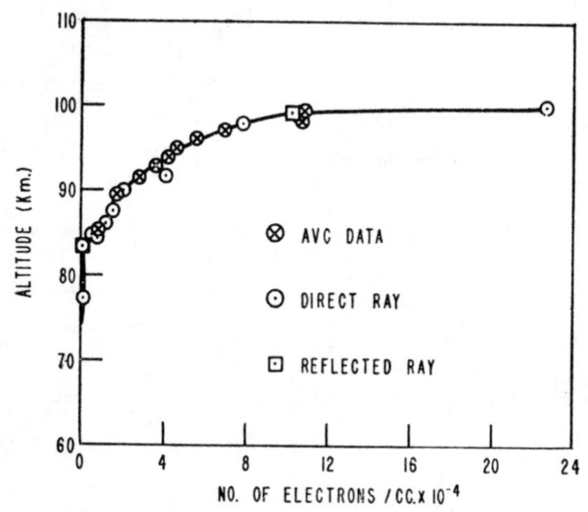

FIG. 5.6—Effective electron density against height obtained with V-2 fired 22nd January, 1948.
(*Courtesy, Naval Research Laboratory and Pergamon Press*)

occurred but at a height of 46 miles (74 km.). These effects were interpreted to indicate a rapidly rising D layer.

With the gradual elimination of the early difficulties, the equipment and techniques were improved so that in 1949 more reliable data started to be assembled. In the flight of the 29th September, 1949, V-2 No. 49, launched 9.58 a.m., peak altitude 94 miles (151 km.), it was found that the heights of the densest parts of the layers are less than those found by the virtual heights method using the *P′-f* curves. The results also indicate that there is a much lower minimum in electron density between the E1 and E2 layers occurring in the winter than in the early autumn.

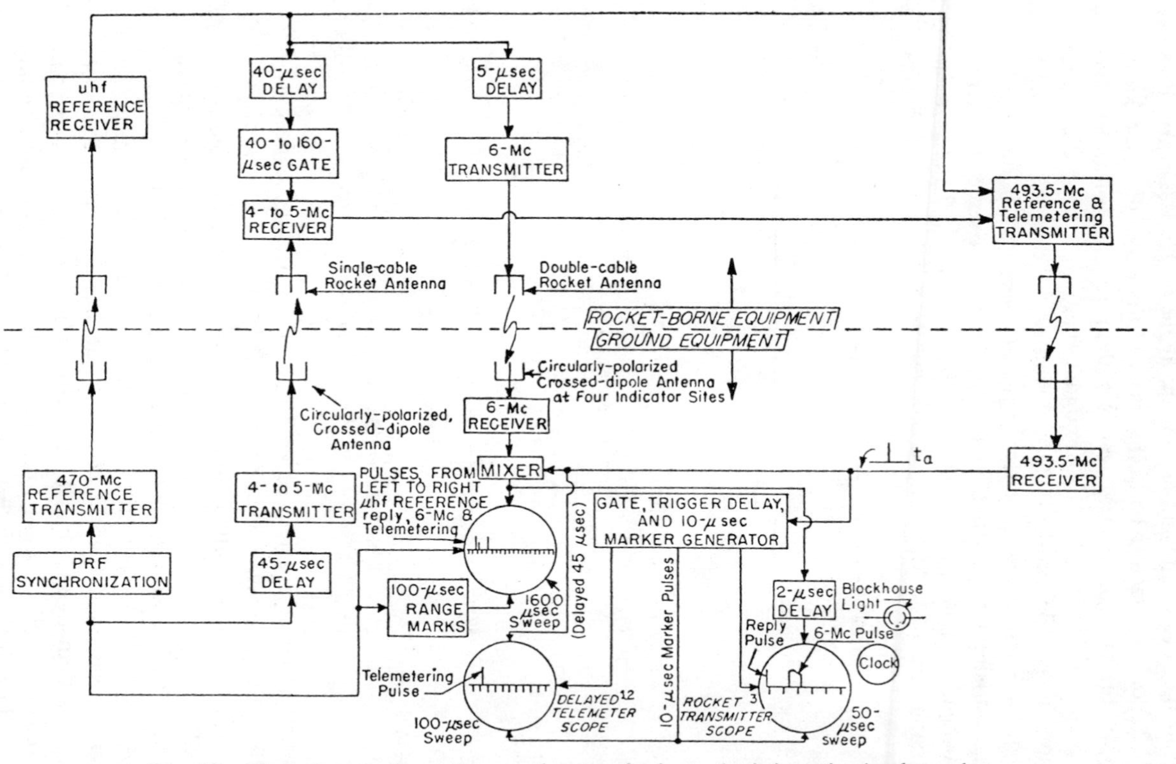

FIG. 5.7—Block diagram for an improved system for ionospheric investigation by rockets.
(*Courtesy, Air Force, Cambridge Research Centre*[2] *and Pergamon Press*)

There have been other workers attacking the problem in the United States besides those of the Naval Research Laboratory. The University of Michigan, for example, in conjunction with the United States Air Force, instrumented some rockets for ionospheric research.[17]

In these experiments the electron density was obtained from measurements of the delay experienced by a pulse on a carrier radio frequency near to the critical frequency (Fig. 5.7). The system employed was to transmit, from two transmitters on the ground, first a high-frequency pulse, followed after 15 microseconds' interval by a low-frequency one. The high frequency was transmitted at 470 Mc/s. and passed through the ionosphere without any delay, whereas the low frequency, near to the critical one, experienced a delay on its path to the rocket. The first pulse on arrival triggered the modulator of the low-frequency rocket receiver and then the outputs were passed to a beacon which gave a long reply pulse of 165 microseconds. The output of the low-frequency receiver put a negative modulation on the reply pulse and the distance of the modulation from the beginning of the pulse was a measure of the delay experienced by the probe signal. A sawtooth-type modulation was also impressed on the long pulse to provide a check on linearity. On this reply pulse were thus the data for the calculations of retardation times. The results were projected on the screen of a cathode-ray tube which was specially designed to facilitate their interpretation.

Although the experiments were initiated also in 1946 like those of the N.R.L., again it was some years before all apparatus had been perfected so that really useful data has not been gathered until recently (Fig. 5.8). The improved equipment now seems capable of giving information which will solve many of the outstanding problems concerning the ionized layers. In addition, by transmitting from the rocket to four widely-spaced ground stations, an attempt is to be made to determine the effects of the Earth's magnetic field on the propagation speed. The problem now is to determine the type of ions and the relative numbers of positive ions, negative ions and electrons.

In this respect the University of Michigan has already used a Langmuir probe technique to check ion concentrations in the lower regions of the ionosphere.[18, 19] A truncated cone at the nose of the rocket was insulated from the body of the rocket and a variable potential difference applied between the two surfaces. By measuring the resultant current flowing between them it was possible to calculate the ion density. The flight on which this experiment was instrumented was that of V-2 No. 28 launched at 2.42 p.m. on 8th December, 1947, in which a peak altitude of 65 miles (104 km.) was reached. Ionization was first detected at 37·5 miles (60 km.), presumably from the D layer and the data was interpreted to mean that there were only positive and negative ions and no electrons. This is at variance with Mitra's estimate that the electron concentration in the D layer is 2×10^2/c.c. Free electrons did not appear until a height of 44 miles (70 km.) was reached. At 65 miles (104 km.) the positive ion concentrations measured with this instrumentation amounted to 10^6/c.c. compared with the electron density of $1{\cdot}5 \times 10^5$/c.c. computed from the *P′-f* data at the height of the E layer on that day, namely at 69 miles (111 km.). This would appear to indicate that there are many more negative ions than electrons in the E layer in accordance with theory.[20] Subsequent experiments are needed to confirm this hypothesis and an excess energy of X-radiation recorded by N.R.L. experiments could account for this effect.[21]

Finally yet another method of tackling the determination of electron density in the ionosphere has been evolved by W. W. Berning[22] of the Ballistic Research Laboratories, Aberdeen Proving Grounds. In an earlier chapter it has been shown how the rockets are tracked by Doppler methods using the DOVAP system. However, this tracking system takes no account of any velocity changes of the radiation which are produced by the ionosphere. At the high frequencies used these variations are only slight, but if a more accurate set of flight data could be obtained and the two trajectories compared it should be possible to analyse the effects of the ionospheric layers. This was done by comparing ballistic trajectories computed for a vacuum, taking data obtained before the ionosphere interfered with the DOVAP results. A number of computations were made, first for the two-stage Bumper-WAC (Fig. 5.9) No. 5 fired at 3.14 p.m. and which reached a peak altitude of 63 miles (100 km.) for the V-2, and 236 miles (378 km.) for the WAC Corporal, and secondly for Viking No. 9 fired at 2.32 p.m. on 15th December, 1952, which reached a peak altitude of 135 miles (215 km.).

The equivalent electron densities found with the Viking (Fig. 5.8) show peaks of 10^5/c.c. at 66 miles (106 km.) (E_1 layer), just over this figure at 77 miles (123 km.) (E_2 layer), with a dip to $2{\cdot}5 \times 10^4$/c.c. between the layers. Finally at 132 miles (210 km.) the equivalent electron density had risen to $5{\cdot}7 \times 10^5$/c.c. These measurements compared very favourably with ground-based measurements of the

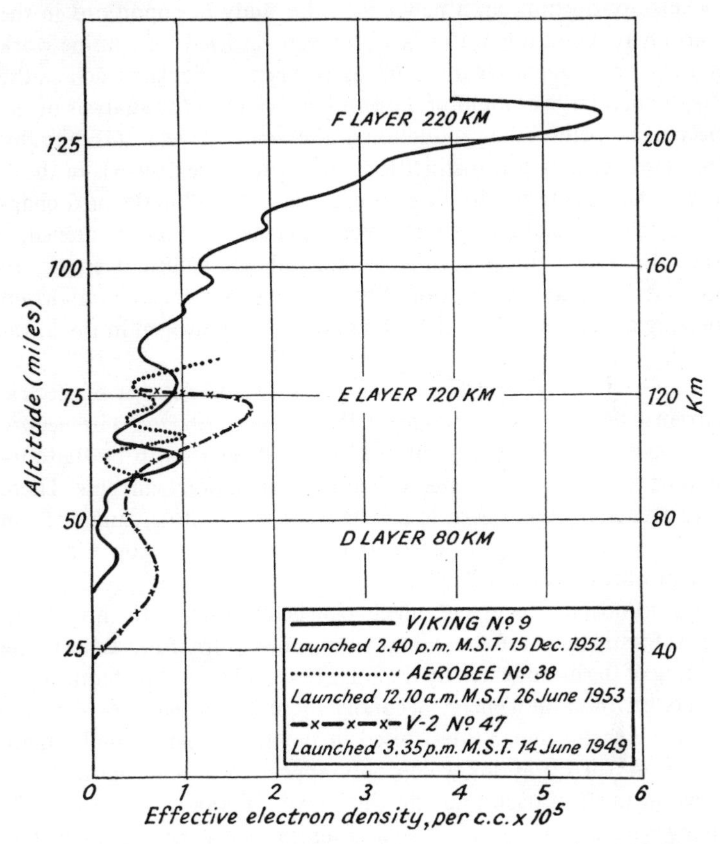

FIG. 5.8—Electron densities obtained with V-2 No. 47, Aerobee, 26th June, 1953 and Viking on 15th December, 1952.

(*After Berning,*[23] *and Lien et al.*[2])

ionized layers, when the E_1 layer appeared as sporadic E and the F_2 layer was falling from 140 miles to 120 miles (230–190 km.) during the flight while at the same time the F_1 layer was fading away.[23]

The Department of Physics, Boston University, has been undertaking the investigation of long-distance communications by sending signals from Virginia to the rockets launched from White Sands. The data received are extremely complex and their interpretation and analysis is now proceeding.

We can see, therefore, that these experiments with high-altitude rockets are opening up a new era in the study of conditions in the ionosphere. Once apparatus has been standardized for routine work and can be frequently carried up by inexpensive rockets such as the Rockoon, a large amount of data will be available for analysis of the mechanism behind the production of the various layers. It is thought, for example, that two distinct ionizing factors are at work in the E region thus giving rise to the bifurcated layer[24] and in the next chapter we shall see that recent experiments to determine X-ray intensities from the Sun in these regions would indicate sufficient energy to account for E-layer ionization. Solar X-rays may thus be important ionizing agents as well as the Lyman series of hydrogen in the ultra-violet.

The ionized layers also act as regions for the passage of electric currents which affect the magnetic field of the Earth.[25, 26] The electric currents above the Earth's surface were first referred to by Balfour-Stewart in 1882 and are often called Balfour-Stewart currents. There have been many theories as to in which layers they flow, ranging from the D region[27] to rings of currents in the equatorial magnetic plane several Earth radii out.[28, 29]

The atmospheric current effects can be classified into three main types. Firstly there are those due to the Sun, a diurnal effect due to the heating of the atmosphere by the solar rays and their direct ionization effects on the atmosphere. Secondly there is diurnal variation due to the solar and lunar tides raised in the atmosphere. Finally there are the storm variations which only appear to depend upon conditions on the Sun itself and can thus have a periodicity due to solar changes such as the synodic solar rotation period of approximately 27·6 days and the sunspot cycle of 11 years.

The diurnal solar and lunar variations have been recorded at many places over the surface of the Earth and it has been possible to obtain a good idea of the distribution of the responsible currents. They are understood to be in the form of sheets, that is currents flowing through layers in the atmosphere which have relatively thin sections compared with their areas. At the equator it is thought that the sheet currents are intensified thus producing a concentrated stream over a limited width. These streams have been termed electrojets.[30] However, the heights of the currents were debatable until rockets were fired into the electrojet over the Pacific Ocean. The

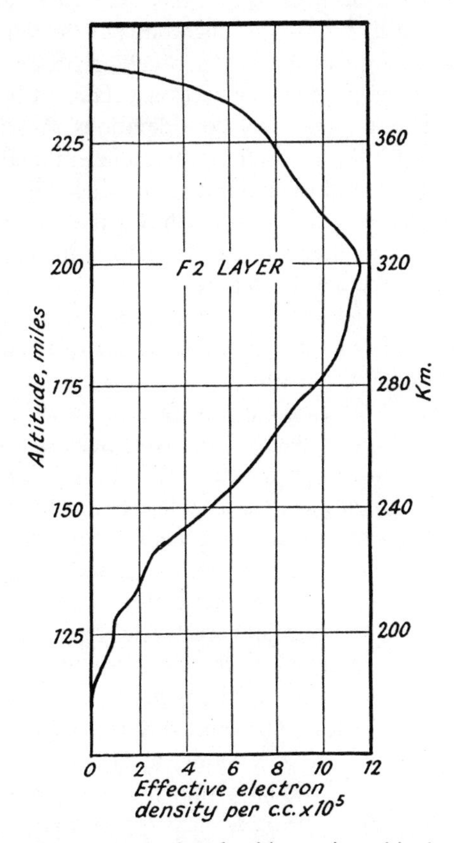

FIG. 5.9—Ionization densities against altitude obtained with the Bumper-WAC fired 24th February, 1949 at 3.14 p.m. M.S.T. showing an increase to maximum in the F2 layer.
(*After Berning,*[23])

electric field in the ionosphere is induced by motions of the conducting layers of the atmosphere produced by tides in the atmosphere.[31] The mechanism is very similar to the induction of electric currents in the armature of a dynamo using a permanent magnetic field and consequently this theory is often known as the dynamo theory. In order to compute the conductivity of the layers it becomes necessary to know the concentrations of the two types of ions, positive and negative, and of the electrons within the layer. The electron density can be determined by radio-pulse methods but the ion densities can only be obtained by calculations of likely processes until rocket instrumentations can produce the necessary data. At one time it was postulated from photo-chemical considerations that the conductivities of the D and E layers would not be sufficient to allow the flowing of currents of the right magnitude to produce the changes in the magnetic field. However, it has been shown that, at least for the E layer, the effective conductivity can be greatly increased. It is well known that where there is an electric field, say E–W, at right angles to a magnetic field, say N–S, ions and electrons will drift together in the same direction but at right angles to the two fields, i.e. vertically at the geomagnetic equator.

This is known as the Hall current. Due to the effects of reduced conductivity at the top of the ionized layer, charges will accumulate and a vertical field will be produced which will stop the Hall current. Moreover, the polarization thus established will have the effect of reducing the action of the magnetic field so that the conductivity E–W will be increased. This effect is most marked at the geomagnetic equator and makes possible the electrojet.

The operation of the electrojet is such that it gives a marked variation in the magnetic force due to the Earth's field. At Huancayo, in Peru, for example, the daily variations are twice those encountered elsewhere at low latitudes. The United States Department of Terrestrial Magnetism has an Observatory at Huancayo and observations over a number of years have shown that the variations due to the electrojet are quite peaked, reaching a maximum between 11.0 a.m. and noon and being almost negligible only a few hours before or after this peak time. It seems, therefore, that the current stream moves round the Earth keeping approximately underneath the Sun.

Accordingly rockets were instrumented to test the electrojet theory.[32, 33] The apparatus used was a total field magnetometer, designed to register the scalar quantity of the magnetic field. An electronic type of magnetometer was employed, consisting of three mutually perpendicular coils with saturable 'permalloy' cores. It was driven by an oscillator and the resultant output signal was proportional to the total magnetic field acting on the coils. This instrument was mounted at the nose of the instrument cone in order to have the magnetometer as far as possible from cables carrying heavy currents. The magnetometer was calibrated every fifteen seconds during the flight and data were telemetered to the ground station.

The first test was made at White Sands Proving Ground in an Aerobee rocket fired at 2.41 p.m. on 13th April, 1948. The rocket attained a peak altitude of 70 miles (112 km.) which is the E layer region. No unusual effects were recorded, the instrument functioned correctly and showed a falling-off of the magnetic intensity with altitude (28 mG.) in accordance with the inverse cube law.

Two more Aerobees were then launched with similar instrumentation from the U.S.S. *Norton Sound* on the geomagnetic equator about 1,000 miles (1,600 km.) west of Huancayo. The first launching, Aerobee No. 10, took place in the late afternoon of the 17th March, 1949. The electrojet current was at that time quite small and, in fact, no variations from the inverse cube law were detected by the instruments in the rocket; the field dropped by about 17·5 mG. at 62·5 miles (100 km.) as expected. Five days later on the 22nd March, 1949, a second Aerobee was launched at 11.20 a.m., Aerobee No. 11; this rocket reached a peak altitude of 69 miles (111 km.). The launching took place when the electrojet variations were at a maximum. The curve of magnetic intensity plotted against height was quite normal until a change of 13·5 mG. at an altitude of 58 miles (93 km.) was reached. Then a marked change of 4 mG. (400 gamma) was recorded over 8 km. until the rocket reached its peak altitude. The same changes were recorded on the downward leg of the flight.

This experiment appears to confirm that the equatorial electrojet does in fact exist (for the change of 400 gamma was the expected change for an electrojet of this nature) and that it occurs in the E layer. Moreover it is not a constant current, but only occurs at the time of maximum magnetic variations on the ground. Other experiments into higher regions of the atmosphere will be required before this can be accepted as the only cause of the diurnal variation although the changes in gamma which were recorded appeared to indicate a magnitude sufficient to account completely for the measured diurnal variation.

The solar storm variations in the magnetic field are known as disturbances. Earlier it has been described how solar flares affect the ionosphere and it is generally agreed that these solar disturbances produce intense currents in the ionized layers, sometimes more than

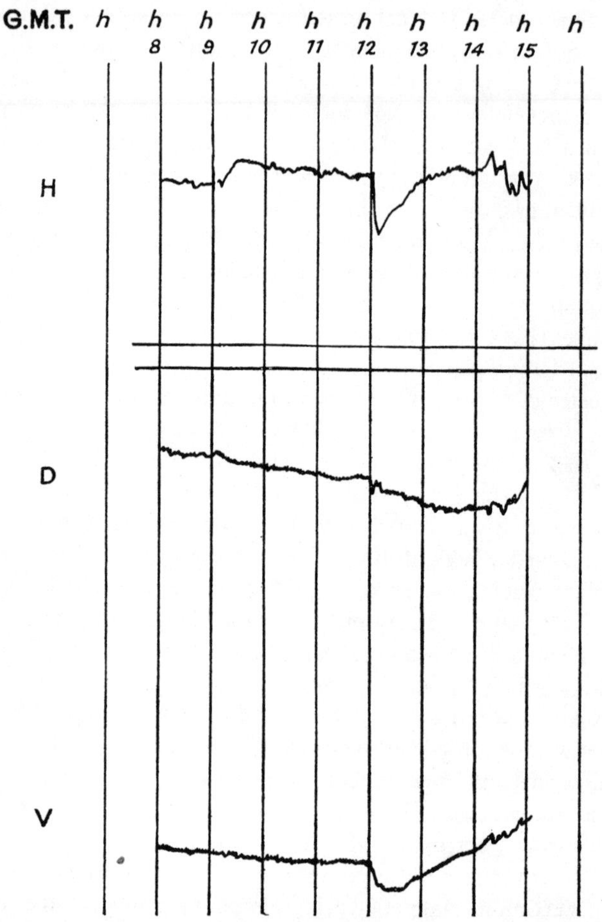

FIG. 5.10—Pen tracing of the photographic record of magnetic elements, 28th February, 1942 which shows the magnetic crochet.
(Courtesy, Royal Greenwich Observatory)

ten times those produced by the diurnal tidal effects. These disturbance current sheets have been analysed.[34, 35] Usually there is a uniform sheet of current over the poles, surrounded by electrojets and then weaker current sheets extending to the geomagnetic equator. The electrojet marks the boundary of the auroral zone which is centred on the geomagnetic pole. Essentially the electrojet system consists of a strong westwards one, on the morning side, meeting a weaker eastwards-flowing one, on the evening side. Where they meet, of course, the currents fall to zero. It is believed that the auroral arc coincides with the electrojets and is caused by intense ionization produced in the upper atmosphere by protons from the Sun. Precisely what are the causes of the electromotive force which produces the current flow remains to be determined. Chapman[36] has proposed that rockets should be fired into the auroral arc and the dark regions surrounding it. This experiment has not yet been tried, but when it is it will undoubtedly yield data which will help to a better understanding of the electrical processes which are taking place in the upper regions of the atmosphere.

REFERENCES

1 Breit, G., Tuve, M. A., *Physical Review*, **28**, 554, 1926
2 Lien, J. R., Marcou, R. J., Ulwick, J. C., Aarons, J., McMorrow, D. R. Ionospheric Research with Rocket Borne Instruments, *Proc. Gassiot Comm.*, Oxford, 1953
3 Nicolet, M., *Memor. Roy. Met. Inst.*, Belgium, **19**, 1, 1945
4 Byram, E. T., Chubb, T. A., Friedman, H., *Physical Review*, **92**, 1066, 1953
5 Bates, D. R., Massey, H. S. W., *Proc. Royal Soc., A*, **187**, 261, 1946
6 Menzel, D. H., *The Observatory*, **70**, 179, 1950
7 Ferraro, V. C. A., *The Observatory*, **71**, 195, 1951
8 Meinel, A. B., *Reports on the Progress of Physics, The Physical Society, XIV*, 121, 1951
9 Bartels, J., *Jnl. Terr. Magnet.*, **39**, 201, 1934
10 Maxwell, A., *The Observatory*, **72**, 22, 1952
11 Smyth, M. J., *The Observatory*, **72**, 236, 1952
12 O'Brien, P. A., *The Observatory*, **73**, 106, 1953
13 *Naval Research Laboratory Report* R-2955, Upper Atmosphere Report No. 1, 1946
14 *Naval Research Laboratory Report* R-3030, Upper Atmosphere Report No. 2, 1947
15 *Naval Research Laboratory Report* R-3294, 1948
16 Seddon, J. C., Propagation Measurements in the Ionosphere with the Aid of Rockets, *Proc. Gassiot Comm.*, Oxford, 1953
17 O'Day, M. D., Upper Air Research by Use of Rockets, *Proc. Gassiot Comm.*, Oxford, 1953
18 Hok, Gunner, Spencer, N. W., Dow, W. G., *Jnl. Geophys. Res.*, **58**, 1953 (June)
19 Reifman, A., Dow, W. G., *Physical Review*, **76**, 987, 1949
20 Massey, H. S. W., *Proc. Royal. Soc., A*, **163**, 542, 1937

[21] BYRAM, E. T., CHUBB, T., FRIEDMAN, H., The Study of Extreme Ultra-violet Radiation from the Sun with Rocket Borne Photon Counters, *Proc. Gassiot Comm.*, Oxford, 1953
[22] BERNING, W. W., *Jnl. of Meteorology*, **8**, 171, 1951
[23] BERNING, W. W., Charge Densities in the Ionosphere from Radio Doppler Data, *Proc. Gassiot Comm.*, Oxford, 1953
[24] LIEN, J. R., *et al.*, *Physical Review*, **92**, 508, 1953
[25] CHAPMAN, S., *The Earth's Magnetism*, Methuen's Monographs, 1936
[26] CHAPMAN, S., BARTELS, J., *Geomagnetism*, Clarendon Press, 1940
[27] MARTYN, D. F., *Nature*, **160**, 535, 1947
[28] CHAPMAN, S., FERRARO, V. C. A., *Jnl. of Terr. Magn.*, **36**, 77, and 171, 1931
[29] FERRARO, V. C. A., *The Observatory*, **71**, 195, 1951
[30] CHAPMAN, S., *Proc. Physical Soc.*, *B*, **64**, 833, 1951
[31] WILKES, M. V., *Oscillations of the Earth's Atmosphere*, Cambridge Monographs, 1949
[32] SINGER, S. F., MAPLE, E., BOWEN, W. A., *Nature*, **170**, 1093, 1952
[33] SINGER, S. F., MAPLE, E., BOWEN, W. A., *Jnl. Geophys. Res.*, **55**, 115, 1950, **56**, 265, 1951
[34] CHAPMAN, S., *Jnl. of Terr. Magn.*, **43**, 351, 1938
[35] VESTINE, LAPORTE, L., LANGE, I., SCOTT, W. E., *Carnegie Inst. of Wash.*, *Publi. No. 580*, 1947
[36] CHAPMAN, S., Rockets and the Magnetic Exploration of the Ionosphere, *Proc. Gassiot Comm.*, Oxford, 1953

Chapter Six

SOLAR RADIATION

⩾ ·ı|ı· ⩽

THE spectrum of the Sun provides scientists with most of the information concerning the one star in the Universe which they are able to observe at close quarters. Unfortunately the Earth's atmosphere, although it appears quite transparent to vision, acts as an absorbing barrier to much of the solar radiation. In consequence a large part of the solar spectrum was completely unknown until the last few years. It has been shown in earlier chapters that the rarefied gases of the upper atmosphere act as a kind of photo-chemical laboratory. Dissociation, excitation and ionization of the molecules and atoms takes place and certain frequencies of solar radiation are absorbed during these processes. Varying types of 'reactions' occur at different levels in the atmosphere, and each absorbs its own portion of the solar spectrum.

The spectral distribution of solar intensity in the lower regions of the atmosphere, that is, in the range of altitudes normally accessible for the construction of solar observatories, is thus a function not only of the radiation characteristics of the Sun but also of the transparent properties of the Earth's atmosphere; and these are both known to be variable.

It is found that atmospheric transmission falls off rapidly beyond 3,000A. Consequently the solar spectrum, when photographed from near to the surface of the Earth, is cut off at about 2,900A, mainly by absorptions caused by the formation of ozone from the oxygen atoms of the upper atmosphere. The presence of this ozone layer has been known for some time, and measurements of it are made from the surface of the Earth by the indirect Umkehr effect method, which enables the vertical distribution of ozone to be ascertained from a critical study of the light scattered from the sky, using a Dobson spectrophotometer.

Accurate measurements of the vertical distribution of ozone made at the highest possible altitudes by instruments carried in balloons or rockets are extremely important in order to permit the checking of the photo-chemical theory of the formation of ozone. Hence the study of the ozonosphere by means of rocket-borne instruments, which can be carried much higher than any in sounding balloons, has been one of the aims of that programme of the Naval Research Laboratory which was concerned with solar spectroscopy in the ultra-violet regions of the spectrum.

The V-2 and other high-altitude rockets penetrate to regions in which there has been little absorption of the sunlight and hence they

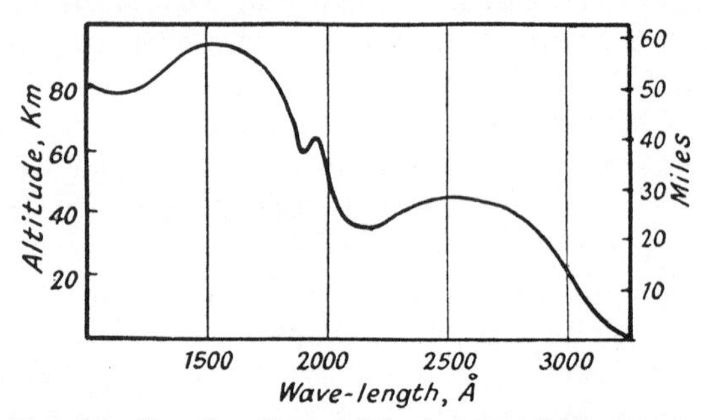

FIG. 6.1—Rough estimate of the heights which must be reached in order to record solar spectra into the extreme ultra-violet.

(*After Naval Research Laboratory*[1])

make possible the investigation of two definite aspects of the rocket solar spectroscopy programme. First there is, of course, the work of the solar physicist, which is primarily that of recording spectra from which new Fraunhofer lines can be identified and thus lead to a better knowledge of the physical processes which are taking place in the atmosphere of the Sun. Then there is the upper-atmosphere physicist who is mainly concerned with the effects of the radiation on the Earth's atmosphere.

Experiments by Erich and Viktor Regener resulted in the recording of ultra-violet solar spectra in 1934. A flight of a sounding balloon from Stuttgart on 31st July, 1934, to an altitude of 19·5 miles (31 km.) carrying an automatic quartz spectrograph, produced a spectrum extending to 2,875A. At the height attained the spectra should, theoretically, have extended to the band 2,100 to 2,200A as reported by Meyer, Schein and Stell, who worked with extremely sensitive photon counters, at the high-altitude observatory on the Jungfraujoch (11,700 feet, 3,580 m.). Another important contribution was that of the manned sounding balloon, Explorer II, which in 1935 obtained spectra down to 2,950A. But these results only served to show the limitation imposed on equipment which could not be carried higher than 20 miles (32 km.) or so. From Fig. 6.1, which shows the heights needed to record spectra into the extreme ultra-violet, it is apparent that the high-altitude rockets can give tremendous improvements. This was quickly realized by the workers in the high-altitude research programme and consequently fairly early the Naval Research Laboratory made spectroscopic work a major project.[1] The intentions were five in number.

(1) To record and identify the Fraunhofer lines in the solar ultra-violet spectrum from 2,900 to 2,100A.

(2) To determine the relative spectral intensity distribution in the solar radiations below the atmospheric cut-off of 2,900A.

(3) To measure accurately the vertical distribution of ozone in the Earth's atmosphere.

(4) To record the solar spectrum in the extreme ultra-violet from 2,000 down to 500A.

(5) The Naval Research Laboratory and the Air Force Cambridge Research Centre also instrumented some rockets to investigate solar spectra into the extreme region, from 100A to what is believed to be the short wavelength limit of the solar spectrum at about 7A.

Although it was realized that the V-2 was unstable after all-burnt and would thus place a limit on the photographic exposures which could be given, an early attempt was made to instrument this rocket with a spectrograph.[1] The instrument used was designed to register solar spectra from 3,000A to 1,000A. Because the rocket could roll, the slit of the normal spectrograph had to be replaced by a system which could obtain solar radiation at varying positions of the rocket relative to the Sun. A transparent bead was used in preference to the more inefficient diffusion screen and it gave a point image of the Sun at most aspects of the rocket. In fact, two such beads were used in the spectrograph. They were of lithium fluoride which can transmit

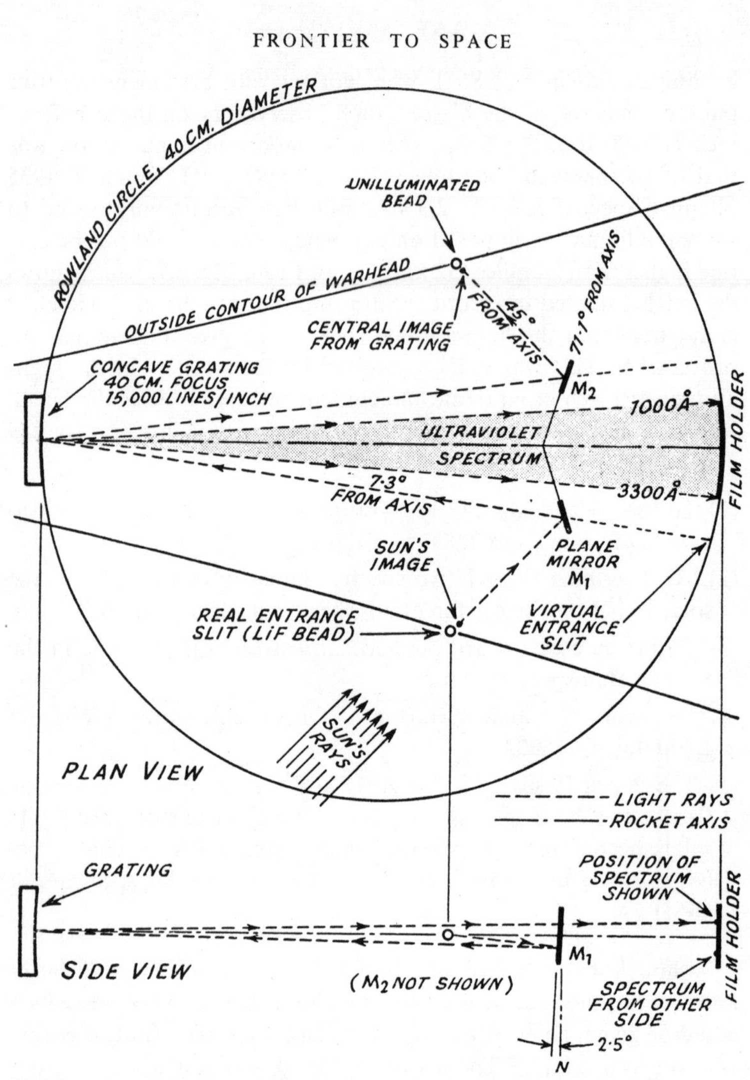

FIG. 6.2—The optical system of the early V-2 spectrograph.
(*Courtesy, Naval Research Laboratory*)

light to a wavelength of 1,100A, and were mounted (see Figs. 6.2, 6.3) on opposite sides of the conical spectrograph so that light from the Sun could be picked up at nearly all orientations of the rocket. Because prisms would not transmit the wavelengths of light which it was desired to record, the dispersal element consisted of a diffraction grating. It was concave, having a radius of curvature of 15·75 inches (40 cm.) and consisted of an aluminized glass blank ruled with 15,000 lines per inch (5,900/cm.). The components of the spectro-

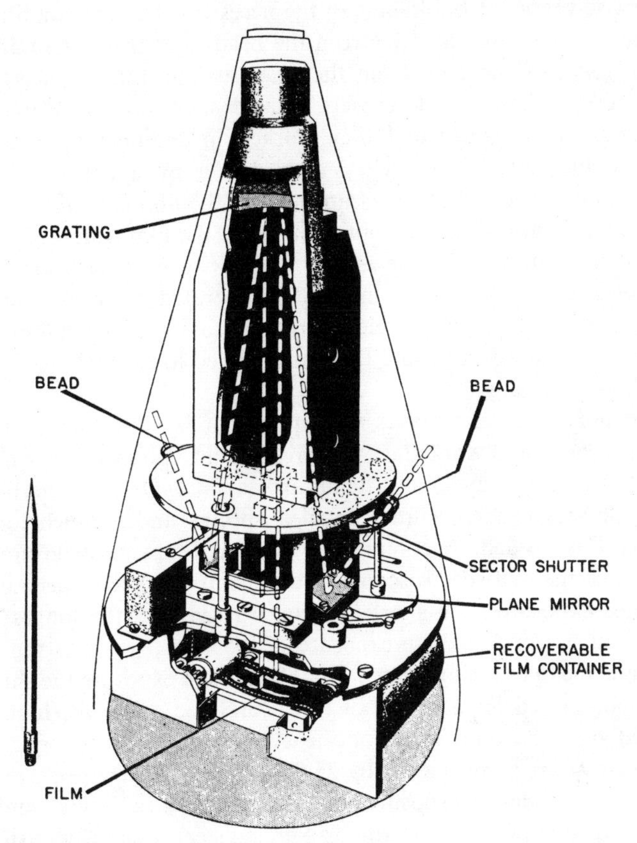

FIG. 6.3—Drawing of the NRL spectrograph showing the positions of the various components.
(Courtesy, Naval Research Laboratory)

graph were so mounted that the first-order spectra fell on the film at the base with a dispersion of 44·1 A/mm.

Two spectra, one from each bead, were photographed side by side on 35-mm. film (Eastman 103–0) where they were dispersed in opposite directions. The film itself was ultra-violet sensitized by overcoating the emulsion with a layer of oil which absorbs ultra-violet and fluoresces in the visible range to which the film is normally sensitive. A specially conductive backing of lampblack had to be used in order to prevent fogging by static electricity which might otherwise become troublesome in the necessary vacuum conditions.

Shutters were mounted between the beads and the plane mirrors which reflected the light from the beads to the diffraction grating (Fig. 6.3). These shutters were rotated so as to give a definite sequence of exposures and they worked in conjunction with the film-winding mechanism. They were driven by a constant-speed motor and connected by an escapement to the film feed. A separate 24-volt D.C. motor pulled continuously on the film which was prevented from moving by the escapement device until each exposure had been completed. A timing switch, operated by a cam on the escapement system, gave a telemetered indication of the completion of each exposure. This could then later be tied to the trajectory data concerning the flight.

Because the rocket moves very quickly it is important that for upper-atmosphere work the exposures should be fairly short if detailed data on the layer constituents are required. On the other hand, solar physics needs accurate detailed spectra and a much longer exposure is needed. A compromise was made in the exposure sequence of the first spectroscopic instrumentation. There was a cycle of three exposures, the shortest being 0·1 sec. and the longest 3·0 secs. with an intermediate exposure of 0·55 sec., which is the logarithmic mean of the other two. Following each exposure the shutter remained closed for a period of just over 1 sec. while the film was moved on. The total time for the cycle was 6·57 secs., and 133 exposures were provided for by 25 feet of film (7·5 metre).

After the series of exposures the film was then rapidly wound up into a cassette made from armour-piercing steel where it was stored in order to survive the impact (Fig. 6.4[*b*]), p. 112.

The first spectrograph to be flown was on the nose of the V-2 launched on 28th June, 1946. This was rocket Number 6 which reached a peak altitude of 67 miles (107 km.). Although arrangements had been made for an airburst and break-up of the missile in flight when descending, the break-up did not occur. The rocket descended nose first and buried itself, creating a great crater in the desert. Recovery of the film was not possible although telemetering had indicated that the exposures had been made correctly.

A subsequent flight of a spectrograph was planned for the V-2 No. 12 launched on 10th October, 1946.[2] It was decided to change the position of the instrument in order to facilitate recovery and it was housed in fin II of the rocket. This spectrograph was similar in design to the one flown on 28th June but the exposure cycle was modified slightly to improve the chances of obtaining a spectrum of the extreme ultra-violet. In it the normal sequence of exposure was to be maintained for 150 seconds, then a long exposure of 100 secs. was to be made. Because the shutters continued to run so as to simplify mechanical arrangements, the effective exposure could only be 55 secs. During this long exposure it was expected that stray light arising from the more intense regions of the spectrum might be troublesome, consequently the normal plane aluminized mirrors were replaced by plane quartz mirrors. But a quartz mirror reduces considerably the light reflected at the longer wavelengths which it was still desired to record during the short exposures of the early parts of the trajectory and it was hence decided to compromise by using one quartz and one aluminium mirror.

The rocket flight on 10th October was a successful one in which the missile reached an altitude of 102 miles (164 km.). Break-up occurred and the spectrograph was recovered in excellent condition on 16th October. The film was sent to the N.R.L. at Washington for processing and thus the first solar ultra-violet spectrum at high altitudes had been obtained. Unfortunately the long exposure had not been successful but the short exposures gave spectra up to an altitude of 55 miles (88 km.), spectra which extended to 2,100A at 34 miles (55 km.). Above that altitude the rocket turned the spectrograph away from the Sun and the extension into the ultra-violet progressively decreased. Excessive vibration of the rocket caused the winding-up mechanism to malfunction, the film was used up too quickly, and the long exposure at the peak of the trajectory was not obtained (Fig. 6.16).

Since these early flights a number of other spectrographs have been flown and many spectra have been obtained. On two V-2 flights in 1947 (V-2 No. 22, 1st April, 1947, and V-2 No. 30, 29th July, 1947) a similar type of spectrograph (Figs. 6.5, 6.6) was used, but it was designed by the Applied Physics Laboratory of the Johns Hopkins University.[3] In it the beads and plane mirrors were replaced by Sun-following ribbed mirrors which gathered light through an

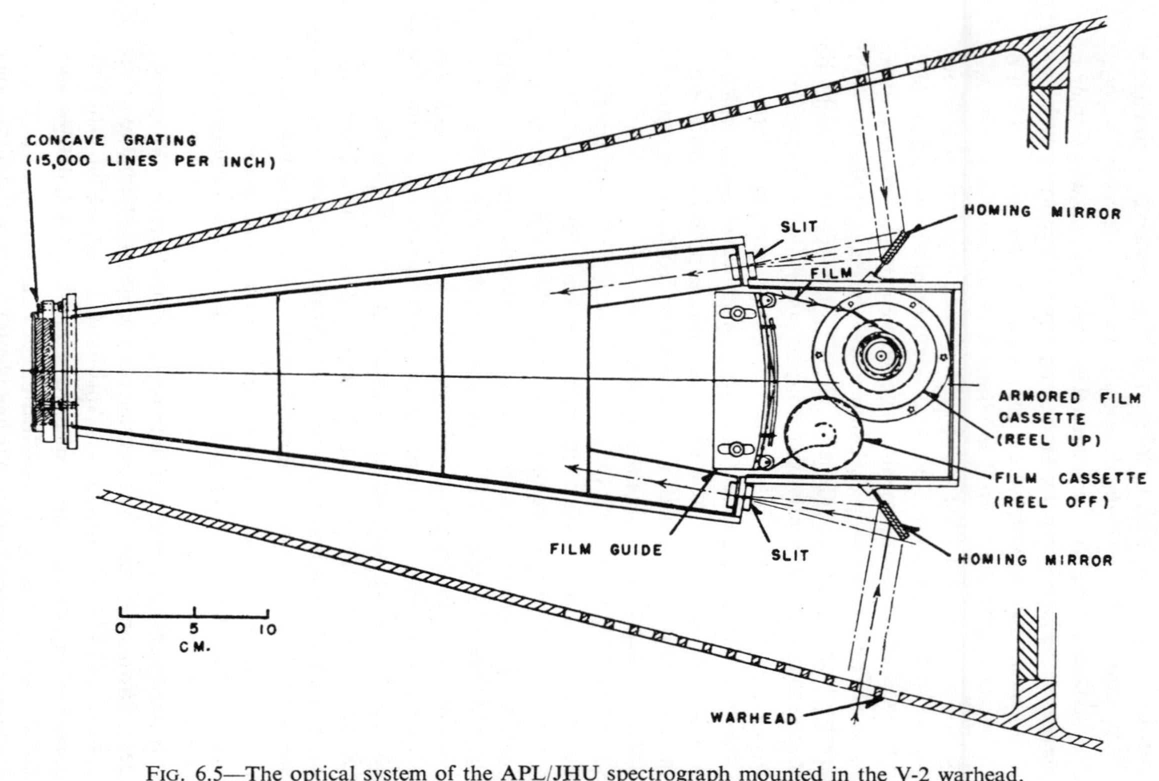

FIG. 6.5—The optical system of the APL/JHU spectrograph mounted in the V-2 warhead.
(Courtesy, Applied Physics Laboratory, Johns Hopkins University)

array of $\frac{1}{2}$-inch (1·27 cm.) holes in the warhead. The light from the Sun was directed by 'homing' mirrors, controlled by photocells, on to slits 0·025 mm. wide and 2 mm. in length. A diffraction grating ruled on aluminized glass with 15,000 lines per inch (5,900 lines/cm.) had a radius of curvature of 19·7 inches (50 cm.). As with the N.R.L. spectrograph, two spectra were formed and were photographed side by side on ultra-violet sensitized film (Eastman Type 103a–0).

The exposures were controlled by a cam-operated switch which gave a series of fourteen five-second exposures during powered flight, followed by five exposures of 55 seconds during the rest of the flight. Examples of spectra obtained are shown in Figs. 6.9 and 6.10. The latest high-altitude spectra have good resolution to about 2,100A, with poor resolution and exposure to 1,850A (Figs. 6.8, 6.12) and traces of the spectrum down to as far as 1,700A or even lower.[4]

The more it is desired to extend the spectrum into the ultra-violet, the greater become the difficulties. This results from the rapid falling-off in intensity of the solar continuum (Fig. 6.14).

By utilizing rocket-borne spectrometers it has thus been found possible to obtain information of extreme importance regarding the Sun. The first important subject for investigation was the solar ultra-violet line spectrum. The fundamental lines of many atoms lie in the ultra-violet range which was investigated in the high-altitude spectroscopic programme. Such elements may play important roles in the processes by which the Sun radiates energy and consequently the results in this region will undoubtedly provide fresh data on the composition and physical states of the layers of the Sun's atmosphere. Of particular interest is the first line of the Lyman series of hydrogen at 1,215·7A. Data on the absorption of this line by air have been obtained in the laboratory but have often been in disagreement. It was calculated that above 60 miles (100 km.) much of the molecular oxygen which is responsible for the absorption would be dissociated into atomic oxygen which should be more transparent and it was hoped that the Lyman alpha line would accordingly be transmitted to the altitudes reached by the rocket-borne spectrograph and could thus be recorded. It was postulated that the line would probably appear as an emission rather than a Fraunhofer one. Later we shall see that this prophecy was justified.

The results of the Fraunhofer line identification in the ultra-violet have been reported in various scientific papers[5, 6] and over 1,000 new lines have been observed (Fig. 6.7). Many of those in the earlier spectra were blends of two or more closely spaced lines. The N.R.L. and the University of Colorado Group and the Applied Physics Laboratory of the Johns Hopkins University, have been working on this programme and have obtained spectra with equipment flown in the three main types of high-altitude rockets. Resolutions of the order of better than 0·3A have been obtained.

Perhaps the most interesting feature of the ultra-violet spectrum discovered to date is the magnesium doublet Mg. II at 2,795·5 and 2,802·7A,[7] having emission lines superimposed on broad absorption lines (Fig. 6.11). These are similar to the H and K lines of calcium in the visible spectrum. The absorption lines are not resolved but appear as two great wings extending over at least 50A and possibly up to 200A on either side of the correct wavelength where there are the two bright emission lines, prominent and very narrow, and very similar to the H and K emission lines in the flash spectrum of the Sun. It is thought that the origin of these emission lines lies in the high-temperature, low-pressure region, high in the atmosphere of the Sun above the reversing layer. Other conspicuous features in the region recorded are the SiI line at 2,882A, MgI at 2,852A (Fig. 6.7), and a number of great dips in intensity which are due to iron multiplets as shown in Figs. 6.9, 6.10, where the iron spectrum is illustrated with the A.P.L. solar ultra-violet spectrum. But a depression from 2,260 to 2,280A (Fig. 6.8) amongst others, could not be explained in terms of strong absorption lines. It is thought that a possible explanation lies in band absorption by unknown constituents of the atmosphere of the Earth or of the Sun. There is definitely a strong band of nitric oxide known in the laboratory between 2,263 and 2,269A which may be affecting the spectrum, and this seemed a likely explanation when the first rocket spectra were obtained. Now, more accurate spectra have shown that it is an unlikely one. Nitric oxide has another band system at 2,150A and there is not a corresponding dip in the solar spectrum. It is concluded therefore that there is not any evidence for the presence of appreciable quantities of nitric oxide in either the atmosphere of the Earth or that of the Sun.[4] The dip remains unexplained.

A swift decrease in intensity is also observed at nearly 2,100A (Fig. 6.12) where oxygen absorption is considered insufficient to account for the weakening. It may be that there are a number of

(*a*) Spectrograph and its shell compared with a one-foot scale.

(*b*) Base of the spectrograph showing the film storage chamber for the recovery of the film after impact.

FIG. 6.4—The NRL Spectrograph.

(*Photos., Naval Research Lab.*)

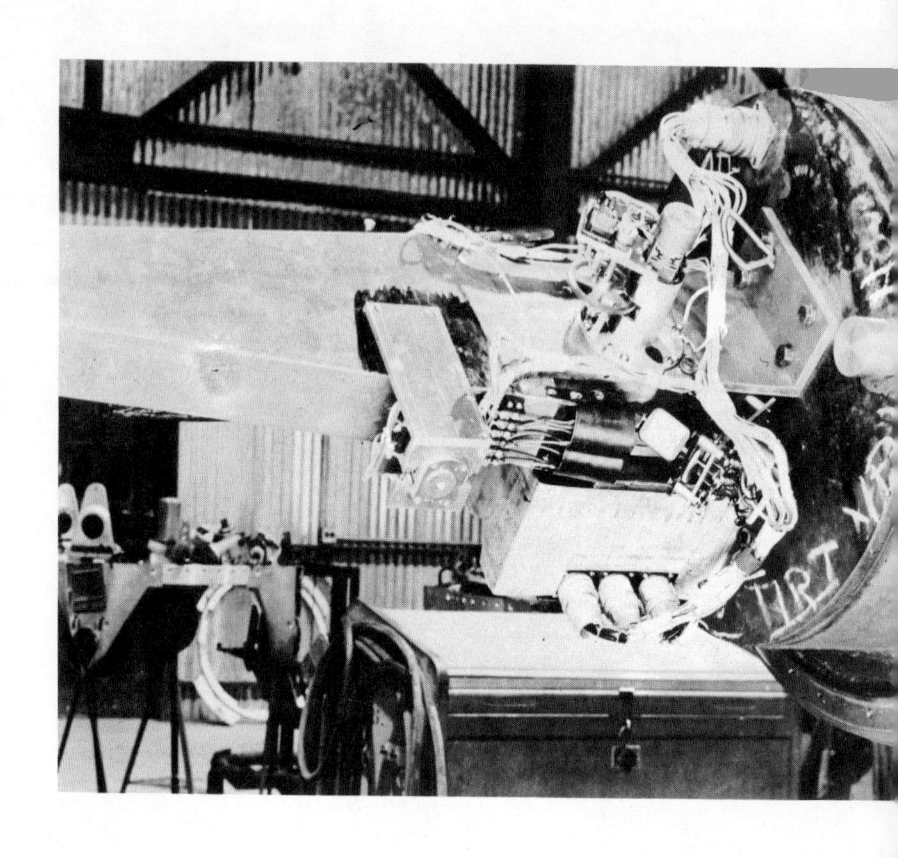

FIG. 6.6—The APL/JHU spectrograph mounted in the nose tip of a V-2 rocket, showing the Sun-following mechanism.

(*Photo., Applied Physics Laboratory, Johns Hopkins University*)

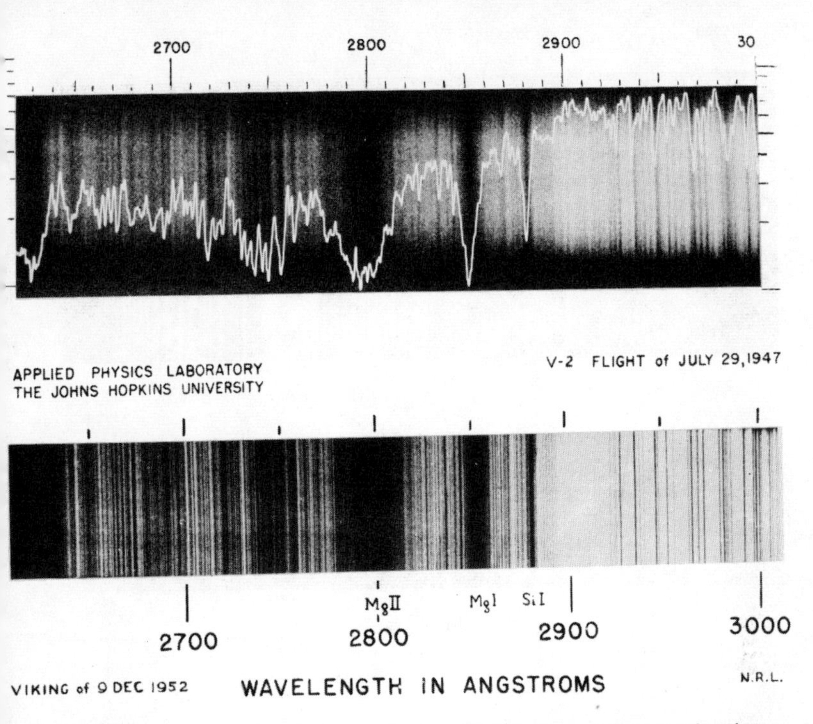

FIG. 6.7—The solar spectrum from 3000 A to 2600 A. *Top*, a photograph taken by the Applied Physics Lab. of the Johns Hopkins University from V-2 No. 30, 29th July, 1947, at an altitude of 96 miles (115 km.). A densitometer trace is shown on this spectrum. *Bottom*, a recent NRL spectrum obtained with a normal incidence 40 cm. radius concave grating. The lines of Mg II, Mg I and Si I are indicated.

(Photos., Applied Physics Laboratory, and Naval Research Laboratory)

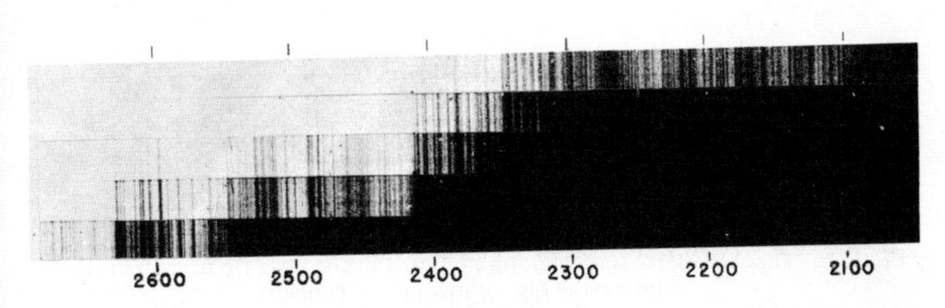

FIG. 6.8—A single spectrum obtained from Viking No. 9 on 9th December, 1952, printed to five different densities in order to bring out the details in the different spectral regions.

(Photo., courtesy Naval Research Laboratory, and Pergamon Press

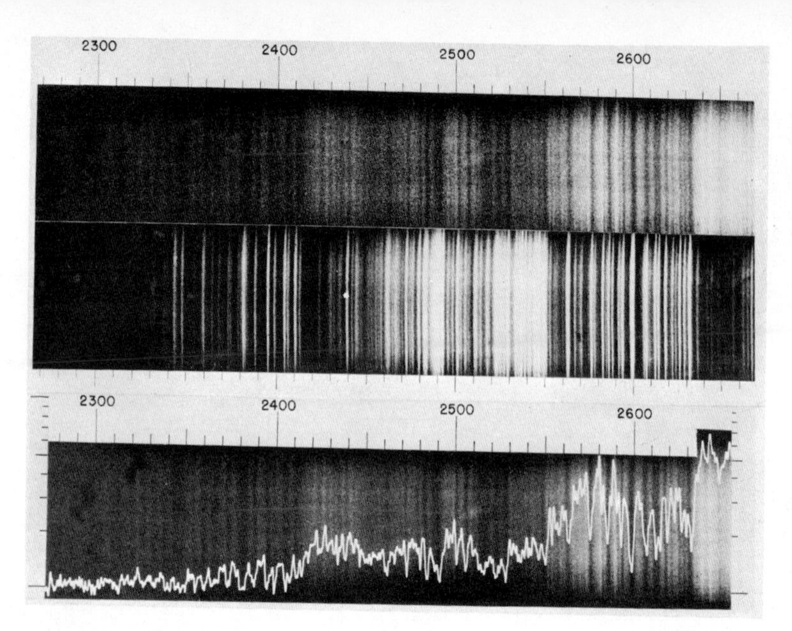

FIG. 6.9.

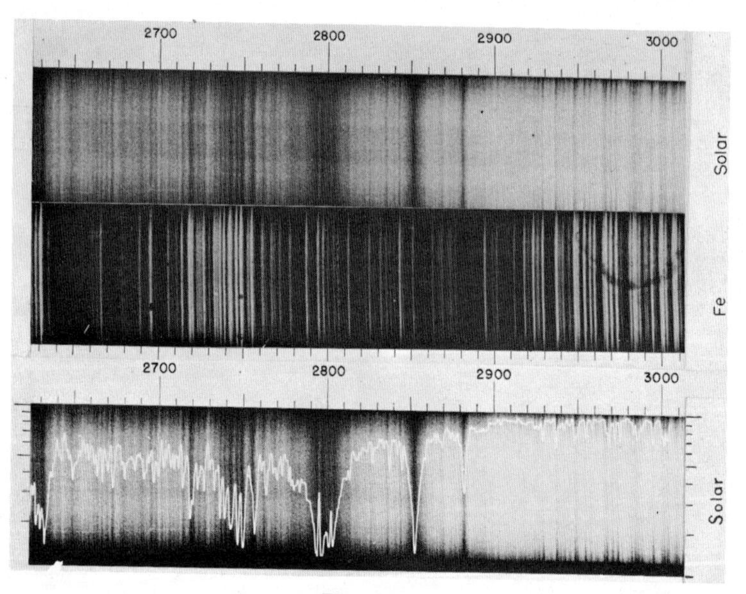

FIG. 6.10.

FIGS. 6.9, 6.10—The solar spectrum from 3000 A to 2300 A compared with the spectrum of iron. The solar spectra were obtained during the flight of V-2 No. 30, 29th July, 1947, by the APL/JHU spectrograph. (*Top*) the solar spectrum; (*middle*) the spectrum of iron; (*bottom*) the solar spectrum with a densitometer trace superimposed, the contours giving an approximation of the relative intensity at different wavelengths.

(*Photos., Applied Physics Laboratory, Johns Hopkins University*

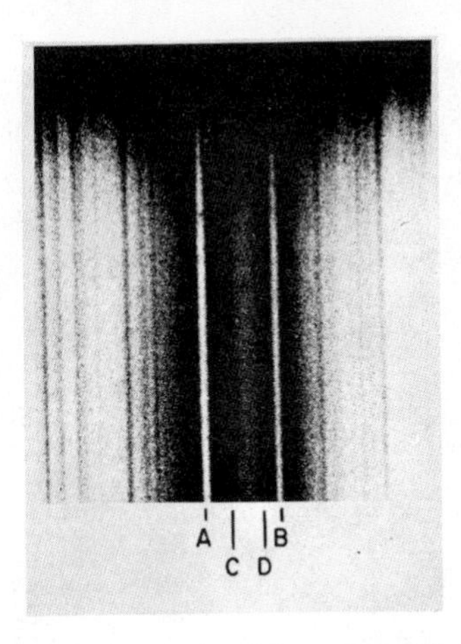

FIG. 6.11—The Magnesium II doublet at 2795 and 2803 A. The bright emission lines are shown at A and B on the top of broad absorption lines. Other absorption lines are faintly visible at C and D.

(Photo, Naval Research Laboratory, courtesy 'Astrophysical Journal')

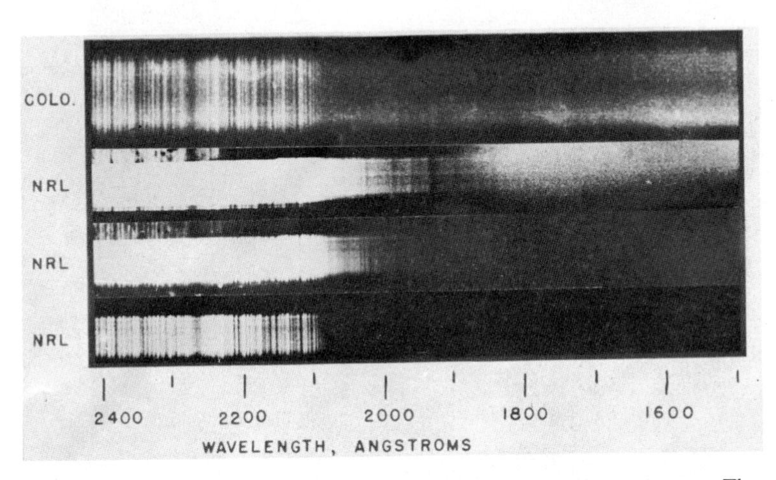

FIGS. 6.12—The extreme short wavelength end of the solar spectrum. The top spectrum was obtained by the University of Colorado while the lower three were obtained with an Aerobee rocket by the Naval Research Laboratory. The spectrum extends to 1850 A and can even be traced to about 1700 A in the second spectrum.

(Photo., courtesy Naval Research Laboratory and Pergamon Press[4]

FIG. 6.13—Bi-axial Sunseeker in Aerobee nose-cone. It is here operating to point towards the Sun while under a ground test. Equipment like this acts as a stable platform to permit long exposure photographs despite tumbling or rolling of the rocket vehicle.

(*Photo., United States Air Force*)

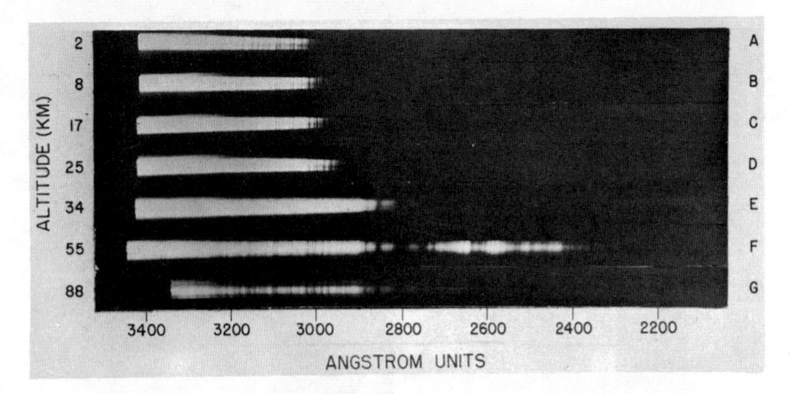

FIG. 6.16—Series of spectra taken from V-2 No. 12, 10th October, 1946. It can be seen how the spectrum extended into the ultra-violet as the rocket rose above the ozone layers.

(*Photo., Naval Research Laboratory*

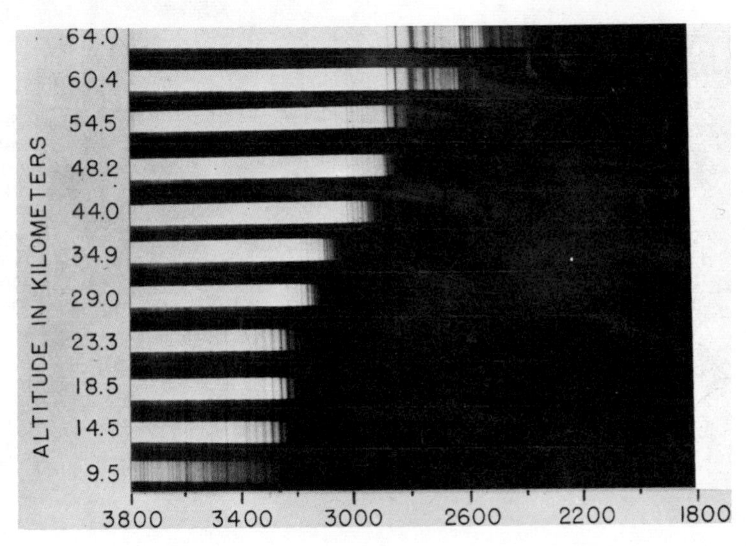

FIG. 6.17—A series of solar spectra made close to sunset by V-2 No. 47, 14th June, 1949. These were used for an accurate determination of the variation of ozone concentration with altitude.

(*Photo., Naval Research Laboratory, courtesy 'Journal of Geophysical Research'*)

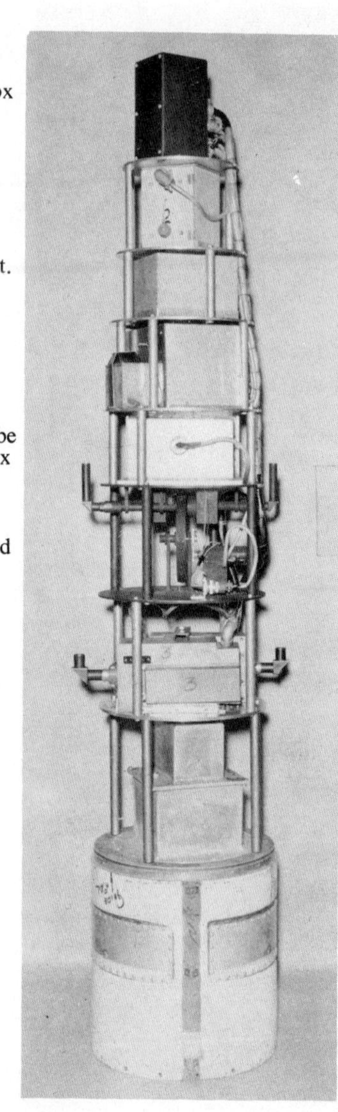

(*a*) (*b*)

FIG. 6.19—(*a*) Aerobee instrumented for determination of day airglow intensity and spectrum. Note how the phototubes look out forward through prisms. This is an overall view of an early instrumentation.

(*Photo., Air Force Cambridge Research Centre*)

(*b*) A close-up of the filter system and of the missile aspect camera as used in Aerobee No. 36, launched 20th May, 1953. The forward-looking prisms are not in place.

(*Photo., United States Air Force*)

strong lines which blend in this region and which cannot be identified because of the broadening due to insufficient exposure. The detail is likewise missing below 2,000A and spoilt completely in both N.R.L. and Colorado spectra by stray light beyond 1,850A although faint traces can be discerned through the fog to about 1,700A (Fig. 6.12).

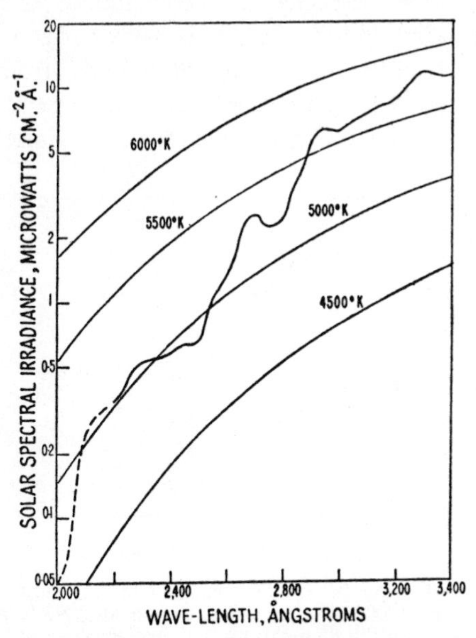

FIG. 6.14—Solar spectral irradiance into the extreme ultra-violet according to latest NRL results. The curve is shown to fall considerably below that for a black body at 6,000°K and well below one of 5,000°K at 2,000 A.
(Courtesy, Naval Research Laboratory)

In order to measure the extension of the spectra into the extreme ultra-violet, longer exposures are needed and they require some kind of stable platform from which the photographs can be made. The University of Colorado had, as part of its contract, the study of the emission spectrum of the Sun into the extreme ultra-violet. The development of a Sunseeker or Sun-follower stable platform was undertaken. The Air Force contracted with the University of Colorado to produce such a device which could be part of the instrumentation of an Aerobee rocket. In December 1952, after many years of study and development, a bi-axial Sunseeker was flown in a rocket.

A grazing incidence ultra-violet spectrometer was carried in the Sun-seeker, and emission spectra of the Sun in the extreme ultra-violet were obtained. The emission Lyman alpha line of hydrogen was obtained as prophesied.

The continuous spectrum has been extended considerably from pre-rocket days. It was expected that a deviation of the solar constant from Planck's radiation law of a simple black body at uniform temperature would occur. The most recent analysis[4] from firings with V-2, Aerobee and Viking rockets show that the intensity of the solar spectrum does fall away rapidly in the ultra-violet and becomes

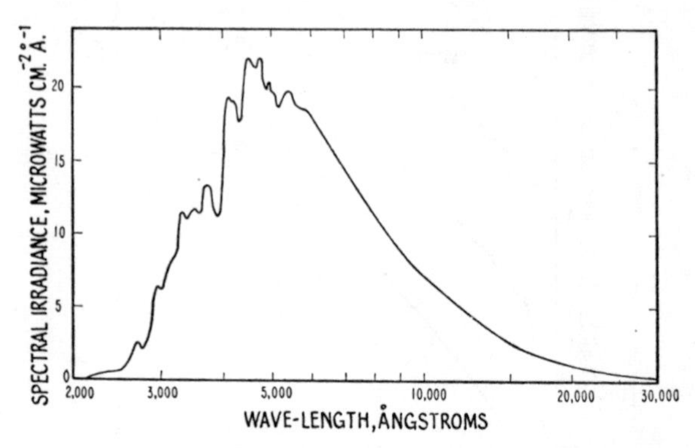

FIG. 6.15—The complete solar spectral irradiance curve from 2,000 A. to 30,000 A established from latest NRL results. From this curve the revaluation of the solar constant at 2·00 calories per square centimetre per minute was made.
(Courtesy, Naval Research Laboratory)

increasingly lower than a 6,000° K. black body (Fig. 6.14). At 2,200A it is below by a factor of 10 and is that for a 4,900° K. black body while at 2,000A it is thought to fall to that of a 4,600° K. black body. Also coming from these results of the solar continuum there is a new evaluation of the solar constant at 2·00 ± 0·04 calories per sq. cm. per minute, as opposed to the normally accepted value of 1·94 (Fig. 6.15).

It is expected that when conditions are right and by using Sun-followers in the perfectly operating rocket, the solar spectrum may be photographed down to 1,000A.

The third aspect of the high-altitude spectroscopy programme was the investigation of atmospheric ozone.[8] A first attempt to do this was made from the series of spectra obtained by V-2 No. 12, launched on 10th October, 1946 (Fig. 6.16). Photographic photometry was used and showed unusual distribution in that a definite second maximum appeared at 10½ miles (17 km.). The total ozone was obtained by integrating the area under the curve of concentration versus height. It was found to be 2·7 mm. compared with the ground measurements of 2·5 mm. for 9th October and 2·7 mm. for 11th October made by the Smithsonian Institute in California. This appeared to be a high value for the total ozone above New Mexico at that time of the year where it would have been expected to be in the neighbourhood of 1·9 mm. It was thought that movement of air masses could create the unusual double peak at the time of high ozone concentration. In this experiment, values of the ozone concentration at the upper edge of the layer were measured for the first time and were found to be in quite good agreement with values as calculated from photo-chemical theory. There was no record obtained of ozone above an altitude of 30 miles (48 km.).

Since that early flight several more experiments have been made including one made in V-2 No. 47 launched 14th June, 1949, close to sunset. The altitude of the Sun was only 1° and consequently the long slant path of the Sun's rays passing through the atmosphere enabled data to be obtained up to an altitude of 49 miles (78 km.) and at lower levels with much greater accuracy than hitherto (Fig. 6.17). Two different designs of spectrographs were used on this flight and one of these comprised two spectrographs in the one housing. Accordingly three sets of independent data were recorded, and agreement between these sets was good.

A Sun-follower was developed by Van Allen.[9] This used a photoelectric method for the determination of ozone concentration. Flown in Aerobee A14 on 23rd June, 1949, and A20 on 25th January, 1951, it employed a ribbed diffusing screen looking out through a quartz plate and reflecting the Sun's light to a spherical focusing mirror. The mirror and screen were driven by a small electric motor so as to follow the Sun. The rays were then reflected from the nose of the rocket into the body of the warhead and thus on to the quartz optics from which the spectrum was dispersed across four photon multiplier tubes covering four channels, 2,647 to 2,657A, 2,924 to 2,934A, 3,108 to 3,124A, and 3,441 to 2,461A. The 'up' and 'down' data agreed quite well on these flights but the results showed higher ozone concentrations than those measured by the Naval Research Laboratory (Fig. 6.18).

From these later results it has been concluded that the double maxima which appeared in the early experiments are really a spurious effect produced by insufficient smoothing of the curves.[10] Because the ozone distribution curve is given by the slope of the total ozone curve it is extremely sensitive to smoothing. On the one occasion

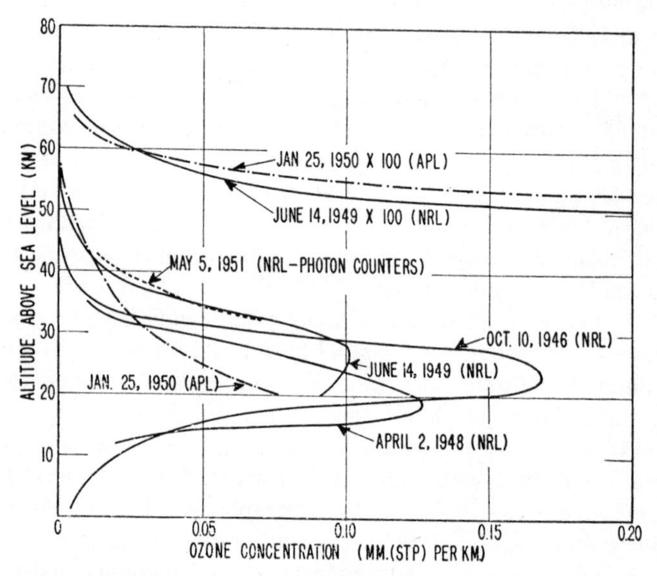

FIG. 6.18—Curves of ozone determinations obtained by rocket experiments. The two determinations which extend to an altitude above 31 miles (50 km.) are shown also on an expanded scale × 100. *(Courtesy, Naval Research Laboratory and Pergamon Press[10])*

when it was possible to make an Umkehr measurement at the same time as the rocket flight (V-2 No. 25, 2nd April, 1948) the results agreed very well indeed. Also photo-chemical calculations have been made and these coincide with the curves obtained from the rocket measurements, especially if rocket data for temperature and density are used.

The most important feature of the collated results from different United States agencies is that the region of the maximum is quite variable both in magnitude and height above the Earth's surface.

It is believed that these variations are due to meteorological conditions or seasonal effects. Sir Charles Norman has shown that in observations made in Western Europe by the indirect method, the ozone concentrations vary with barometric pressure at ground level. Ozone concentrations are low in high-pressure regions and high in low-pressure regions.

In addition to spectroscopic work with photographic apparatus, measurements of the solar spectrum at definite wavelengths have been made with photon counters.[11] Since 1949 the Naval Research Laboratory have been instrumenting V-2 rockets and Aerobees with these intruments. The data were telemetered and thus gave a continuous record of intensity versus altitude to heights in excess of the absorbing layers. The best results and most accurate data were obtained from the newly recorded hydrogen Lyman alpha line at 1,216A.[12] On four flights this radiation was detected at an altitude of about 50 miles (80 km.) by a grazing incidence concave grating spectrograph and the results have indicated that in the 1,180 to 1,300A region the main solar radiation is given by the hydrogen Lyman alpha emission.[13] The width of this emission line is indicated as being less than 1A. There is an absorption window in the O_2 absorption spectra which is extremely narrow, the absorption increasing by as much as 200 per cent at only 1A on either side of the Lyman alpha line.[14] The absorption of this radiation by nitric oxide may provide the D layer ionization[15] and the rocket data do not completely exclude such a possibility. An absorption by nitric oxide of only one per cent of the hydrogen Lyman alpha radiation recorded by the rockets would give a rate of ion production of the correct order of magnitude for the production of the D layer, and the amount of nitric oxide required would still be well within the limits imposed by the spectral studies of its abundance.

The Lyman continuum of the solar radiation probably originates in the chromosphere which, according to Nicolet, except for Lyman alpha, radiates most strongly from 910A to shorter wavelengths.

In one experiment with photon counters at 1,500A there was an indication that a rapid transition from molecular to atomic oxygen took place at a height of about 60 miles (100 km.).[16] Improved instruments are being devised to check this.

Finally measurements have been made into the far ultra-violet regions of the solar spectrum. Recent developments in radio astronomy and the investigation of the coronal lines of the Sun have indicated that the outer atmosphere of the Sun attains temperatures in the order of millions of degrees. Although this is a kinetic temperature rather than the type of temperature which we use in engineering processes on Earth, it enables a computation to be made of the maximum energy transmission from this region as being below 50A in the soft X-ray region of the spectrum. Nicolet has suggested that the corona radiates between 20 and 60A. The first attempt to measure X-radiation was made with X-ray packets. These consisted of a photographic film mounted between brass plates like a sandwich. One of the plates had a window in which a step wedge of different thicknesses of aluminium was used to block visual and ultra-violet light yet permit selective recording of X-rays between 8 and 12A. Later uses of other materials in the wedge was expected to permit the study of the X-ray spectrum in more detail. These packets were not successful because the rockets in which they were flown did not reach sufficient altitude to penetrate the absorbing layers.

However, several rockets were instrumented with photon counters to measure X-radiation,[17] and showed that the Sun indeed emits X-rays[18] which are absorbed by the gases of the Earth's upper atmosphere thus producing the E-layer. V-2 No. 49 launched 29th September, 1949, included in its instrumentation two photon counters sensitive to X-rays below 10A and the radiation was in fact detected first at 54 miles (87 km.)[19] and then progressively increasing with altitude up to 90 miles (145 km.).

X-ray photon counters were later flown in two Aerobee rockets which were launched in May 1952 and these counters recorded definite X-radiation at altitudes beyond 55 miles (90 km.).

But the most extensive experiment was planned for and flown in the Viking No. 9 launched in December 1952. This rocket attained a peak of 135 miles (215 km.) but excessive roll and faulty telemetering reduced the useful data to a very small amount. Nevertheless rapidly increasing X-ray intensity was recorded above 10A in the E layers. One of the photon counters had a window of 0·25 mil. and thus responded to a band from 8 to 18A. It counted X-rays at a rate equivalent to an incident flux of about 0·8 erg/cm.^{2}/sec. Still softer radiation was measured by two photon counters using thin films of nitrocellulose as windows. The total flux of X-radiation within a band 10 to

60A amounted to about 1·0 erg/cm.^{2}/sec. These latest N.R.L. results[20] show that the solar X-ray spectrum is of an order of magnitude sufficient to account for all the E-layer ionization which needs a flux of 10^{-1}erg/cm.^{2}/sec. to account for the electron density of 2×10^5/c.c. The flux is summarized in the following table:

Band as measured	*Flux of X-radiation*
7–10A	10^{-3} to 10^{-4} erg/cm.^{2}/sec.
8–18	0·8
10–60	1·0

High-energy photons (i.e. X-rays) have been shown by Chondburg[21] to need an energy of 181 e.v. to account for E layer ionization in addition to the normally accepted pre-ionization of O_2.

The night airglow has long had the attention of upper-atmosphere physicists and astronomers and many measurements have been made with apparatus based on the ground. This was not possible, however, with a suspected day airglow because of the obscuring effects produced by the great scattering of the sunlight in the lower atmosphere. With rockets ascending to high altitudes above the scattering layers, it became possible to make an attempt at instrumentations designed to measure day airglow. This was done by the Air Force Cambridge Research Centre.[22] A photomultiplier tube (R.C.A. 1P21) was used as the detecting unit and varying dynode voltages, changed by a rotary switch, together with load resistors between 1 and 5 megohms, enabled sensitivities to be varied as much as 250 times. The outputs were taken via cathode followers and passed to the telemetering system. Because of the large voltages required for the photo-tubes (obtained from banks of 30-V and 15-V hearing-aid batteries) the whole unit was mounted in a pressurized container.

The light to be measured was taken from a direction parallel to the axis of the rocket through a right-angle prism in a collimator tube which extended through the skin of the rocket. The field of view covered was two or three degrees and interference filters, mounted on a rotating disk, enabled measurements to be made of the energy contained in regions 150A wide at eight points in the visible spectrum. This equipment was flown with slight modification, e.g. fixed filters were used in three rockets; the successful flights were V-2 No. 51 launched 31st August, 1950, which reached an altitude of 85 miles

(136 km.), Aerobee Rocket, 25th July, 1951, and Aerobee Rocket, 20th May, 1953.

The sky light was found to decrease rapidly and nearly exponentially from ground level to about 22 miles (35 km.) and it seems to be due mainly to Rayleigh scattering. Beyond 22 miles (35 km.), however, the value remains constant, independent of altitude. This day airglow has a magnitude of approximately 10,000 times the night airglow and is, indeed, about three per cent of the daytime ground value, remaining constant from 22 to 85 miles (35–136 km.). It differs from the night airglow in its spectral intensity and distribution. In the night glow most of the lines and bands except the green oxygen line, 5,577A are increased by direct solar radiation, that is, at dawn and sunset. These are the familiar red oxygen lines at 6,300A and 6,363A, sodium line 5,893A, negative bands of nitrogen at 3,914A and OH bands at 6,560A. It seems definite that the atoms and molecules of the upper atmosphere are excited by resonance radiation from the Sun during the daytime. The night glow generally consists of rather a weak continuous background with widespread emission lines and bands of much greater intensity. A spectrum of this nature is not found for the day glow by the rocket-borne instruments. It is thought that further investigation should be made of whether or not the intensity of the day airglow correlates with the build-up of electron density in the ionosphere.

Rocket-borne instruments are gradually amassing a wealth of information concerning the radiation from the Sun, but it will be many years before astronomers and solar physicists are able to sift this data and give us a more accurate model of solar activity and processes. Moreover, it will be a decided advantage if cheaper rockets are able to carry out synoptic observations of solar radiation.

REFERENCES

[1] *Naval Research Laboratory Report* R-2955, Upper Atmosphere Report No. 1, 1946

[2] *Naval Research Laboratory Report* R-3030, Upper Atmosphere Report No. 2, 1946

[3] FRAZER, L. W., *Bumblebee Report No.* 153, Aplied Physics Laboratory, Johns Hopkins University, 1951

[4] JOHNSON, F. S., PURCELL, J. D., TOUSEY, R., WILSON, N., The Ultra-violet Spectrum of the Sun., *Proc. Gassiot Comm.*, Oxford, 1953

[5] DURAND, E., OBERLY, J. J., TOUSEY, R., *Astrophysical Journal*, **109**, 1, 1945

[5] HOPFIELD, J. J., CLEARMAN, H. E., Jr., *Physical Review*, **73**, 877, 1948

[7] PURCELL, J. D., TOUSEY, R., WILSON, N., *Astrophysical Journal*, **117**, 238, 1953
[8] JOHNSON, F. S., PURCELL, J. D., TOUSEY, R., *Jnl. Geophys. Res.*, **56**, 583, 1951, **57**, 157, 1952
[9] VAN ALLEN, J. A., *Proc. Gassiot Comm.*, Oxford, 1953
[10] JOHNSON, F. S., PURCELL, J. D., TOUSEY, R., Studies of the Ozone Layer above New Mexico, *Proc. Gassiot Comm.*, Oxford, 1953
[11] FRIEDMAN, H., LICHTMAN, S. W., BYRAM, E. T., *Physical Review*, **83**, 1025, 1951
[12] BYRAM, E. T., CHUBB, T., FRIEDMAN, H., The Study of the Extreme Ultraviolet Radiation from the Sun with Rocket Borne Photon Counters, *Proc. Gassiot Comm.*, Oxford, 1953
[13] RENSE, W. A., *Physical Review*, **92**, 850, 1953
[14] WATANABE, K., MARMO, F., INN, E. C. Y., *Physical Review*, **90**, 155, 1953
[15] BATES, D. R., SEATON, M. J., *Proc. Physical Soc., B*, **63**, 129, 1950
[16] FRIEDMAN, H., LICHTMAN, S. W., BYRAM, E. T., loc. cit., 11
[17] BYRAM, E. T., CHUBB, T. A., FRIEDMAN, H. *Physical Review*, **92**, 1066, 1953
[18] BURNIGHT, T. R., *Physical Review*, **76**, 165, 1949
[19] FRIEDMAN, H., LICHTMAN, S. W., BYRAM, E. T., loc. cit. 11
[20] BYRAM, E. T., CHUBB, T., FRIEDMAN, H., Solar X-rays and E Layer Ionisation, *Proc. Gassiot Comm.*, Oxford, 1953
[21] CHONDBURG, D. C., *Physical Review*, **88**, 405, 1952
[22] BEDINGER, J. F., Day Air Glow with Rocket-Borne Photometers, *Proc. Gassiot Comm.*, Oxford, 1953

Chapter Seven

COSMIC RAYS AND THE DEBRIS OF SPACE

⋙ ⦀ ⋘

THE existence of cosmic rays was suspected when in 1901 it was observed that a closed ionization chamber would exhibit signs of conductivity. When all possible sources of ionization had been accounted for it was postulated by C. T. Wilson that this ionization might be produced by intense naturally occurring radiation which had hitherto been undetected. Attempts were then made to prove this hypothesis and tests which were made at the tops of mountains appeared to confirm that the radiations did not emanate from the Earth because there was no diminution of intensity with altitude. In fact, by 1910, it had been found by Hess from balloon ascents that the intensity increases with altitude, and later it was ascertained that the intensity of the radiation reaches a peak value at about 17 miles (27 km.) and then falls.

Rocket measurements have shown that this fall in intensity continues until an altitude of around 35 miles (55 km.) is reached when the intensity becomes constant. This indicates that 35 miles (55 km.) is the top of the appreciable atmosphere as far as cosmic rays are concerned.

At first it was thought that the cosmic rays consisted of extremely short-wave gamma radiation, but observations of their deviation in the presence of magnetic fields such as that of the Earth or by artificially produced fields, indicated that they are corpuscular in nature and are electrically charged.

Cosmic rays are recorded by several methods. The principal tool is the ionization chamber and developments therefrom. Essentially this consists of a cylinder having two electrodes, one being the surface of the cylinder, the other an insulated wire passing down the centre. Ionization chambers measure the rate of ionization. A development from these is often known as the Geiger-Müller counter. The electrodes are at a potential just below that which would cause a glow discharge in the chamber and when a cosmic-ray particle enters, it produces electrons and ions which, in turn, are accelerated and produce other electrons and ions, so that a momentary surge of current flows through the counter and can be recorded by suitable circuitry. By using alcohol vapour in the counter it can be made self-quenching so that particles arriving swiftly one after the other can be detected individually and counted. A proportional counter operates at a lower potential than the Geiger-Müller counter and is able to differentiate between the various energies of the ionizing particles because the pulse of current becomes proportional to the particle energy.

If a series of counters are arranged geometrically so that they only operate the counting circuit if a particle passes through all of them 'simultaneously' the arrangement becomes known as a cosmic-ray telescope and it is capable of detecting the direction from which the particles are travelling. By using screens of lead it is also possible to measure the energy of the radiation and to study its effects on matter.

Another method of detecting cosmic rays is by their effects upon photographic emulsion. Special photographic plates are exposed to the radiation which acts on the atoms of the emulsion and produces ionized tracks which, after development of the plates, are visible when examined under a microscope.

A further method is to use what is known as a Wilson cloud chamber. The chamber is filled with saturated air which is suddenly expanded by means of a piston. This expansion causes the air to cool so that it becomes supersaturated and the water condenses on any ions which are present. Consequently if an ionizing particle has passed through the chamber immediately prior to the expansion, the path is indicated by water droplets (clouds) formed on the ions which the particle has produced along its path. Lead plates and magnetic fields enable workers to find out a great deal concerning such ionizing particles. In practice, Geiger tubes are linked with the cloud chamber to trigger its expansion whenever they register the passage of an ionizing particle through the chamber. At the same time they control a photographic flash which enables the path to be photographed. Arrangements of two cameras can produce stereoscopic pictures of the tracks.

By means of devices such as these much information has been collected concerning cosmic rays. It is known that they come to Earth from space but their origin is still very much in doubt. It is known, too, that the Earth's magnetic field has a decided effect upon them, as it does upon the charged corpuscles responsible for the aurorae, and from this it has been determined that they are definitely charged particles and not radiation. It was concluded that the primary particles which enter the Earth's atmosphere are protons, but in 1948 it was discovered that much heavier particles were present in the primaries.[1, 2] The cosmic radiation is now assumed to consist of the stripped nuclei of the atoms of the elements existing in much the same relative abundance as these atoms are present in the universe[3]; namely there is a preponderance of protons, then helium nuclei and so on up the atomic scale. So far, particles as heavy as iron (atomic number 26) and tin (atomic number 50) have been identified.

The kinetic energy of the cosmic-ray particles is extremely high and while these nuclei might have orbital electrons in space, such electrons would be immediately stripped as the primaries encountered any absorber. Consequently the heavy primaries are multiply ionized (to 26-fold and 50-fold ionizations in some cases) and accordingly they have high energy dissipations along their paths through the atmosphere.

One mechanism by which the primaries can lose energy as they enter the atmosphere is by interaction with the orbital electrons of the atmospheric gases. This produces ionization and the energy of the particle can be slowly dissipated in this way. Yet other high-energy primaries suffer what is known as a catastrophic collision or star production, occurring from the collision of a primary with an atomic nucleus. Most high-energy primary particles end their lives this violent way.

At 15 miles (24 km.) all the primaries have interacted with the atmospheric gases and produced other particles such as mesons, neutrons, photons, electrons and positrons. These multiply to such an extent that the impact of a single high-energy primary on the top of the atmosphere can produce a shower of less energetic particles which can cover a circle of about one mile in radius at sea level.

The Earth's magnetic field sorts out primaries of different energies. For example, if the kinetic energy of the particle is not sufficiently great, it can be turned back and prevented from reaching the atmosphere. Accordingly it is found that there is quite a latitude effect on the distribution of the energies of incoming cosmic-ray particles. Particles of high energy can enter anywhere, whereas low-energy particles can only come into the atmosphere at high latitudes. In this connexion measurements at various parts of the Earth's surface have revealed a peculiar effect, namely that the energy spectrum of the cosmic rays has a definite lower cut-off point at about 1 Bev and there is no observed latitude dependence above 50° to 60°.

Two possibilities are suggested, firstly that there are no very low-energy primaries, or secondly, that the heliocentric field is screening them from the Earth. If this latter is the case, the heliocentric field at the distance of the Earth from the Sun must be equal in intensity to the Earth's own field at a latitude of about 55°. Since the low-energy primary is regarded as representing the greatest biological hazard[4] efforts will be made with rockets to determine if these primaries do, in fact, exist. The deep-space probe rocket which will be described in the next chapter will be invaluable for this purpose.

Because most particles approach the Earth from the west it is confirmed that they are essentially positively charged, and the highest energy primaries have an energy of 800 Bev.

The investigation of cosmic rays at high altitudes has several distinct aspects. Firstly is the search for the origin of the rays which will only be successful when man has a full understanding of their peculiarities and true nature. Secondly there are the biological hazards to high-altitude and space flight. Thirdly there is the study of the reaction of the primaries in matter which adds to the knowledge of high-energy nuclear reactions of the type which man cannot yet reproduce artificially.

The first cosmic-ray experiment with rockets consisted of coincidence counts and determinations of the relationship between hard and soft components as a function of altitude. The chance of a primary particle reaching the Earth's surface is less than one in a thousand and the rocket is the only way of getting physical instruments to the outer regions of the atmosphere where cosmic-ray primaries can be studied in their original state.

Early experiments were made by the Johns Hopkins University Applied Physics Laboratory and were concerned solely with counting rate as a function of altitude. The rockets used were V-2s numbered nine, 30th July, 1946, seventeen, 17th December, 1946, twenty-two,

1st April, 1947, and twenty-three, 8th April, 1947, reaching peaks between 64 miles (102 km.) and 116 miles (186 km.). The counters were not screened from shower production in the material of the rocket, but in V-2 No. 30, fired 29th July, 1947, to a peak of 100 miles (161 km.), a counter was placed in a long bakelite tube which projected forward of the rocket. A maximum counting rate of 49 counts per second was recorded at 12·4 miles (19·8 km.) while above 34 miles (55 km.) the rate was constant at 22·4 counts per second.[5] Subsequently single counter experiments were made in V-2 No. 35, 27th May, 1948, and Aerobee A-5, 5th March, 1948, and similar results were obtained. The data from three flights are shown averaged in Fig. 7.5.

The success of the Bumper-WAC was followed by an offer by the General Electric Company to the Applied Physics Laboratory to use Bumper No. 6 for a single counter experiment. The counter was mounted in the nose-cone of the WAC Corporal. Unfortunately when the two-step was fired on 21st April, 1949, an incorrect trajectory made it necessary to terminate propulsion too quickly for a high altitude to be reached.

In addition to this work the Applied Physics Laboratory flew some telescopes. An albedo of low-energy particles and of electrons was detected rising from the topmost regions of the effective atmosphere and produced by the impact of the primaries. From the telescope work it was also deduced that from a vertical direction the flux of cosmic rays amounted to 0·078 particles per second per square centimetre per steradian.

The production of bursts was investigated. The rate was found to increase with height above sea level, reaching maximum value above the effective atmosphere, and showing that the bursts are caused by the first interaction of the primaries with matter. Tests of cosmic-ray intensity were, moreover, made by Aerobees launched at the geomagnetic equator, in the Gulf of Alaska (58° N.) and off the coast of Washington (50° N.).

Cosmic-ray experiments were also instrumented by the Naval Research Laboratory. The Geiger counters used in their early V-2 experiments[6] were normally operated at 1,000 volts and utilized alcohol vapour to make them self-quenching. Recording was by telemetering stored counts and also by a photographic technique using a bank of neon tubes to register flashes on a moving film. The Geiger counters were arranged in the form of a telescope (Fig. 7.1) so that a cosmic ray would operate several counters in line. This would be indicated by a coincidence in the time of discharge of the counters which had been traversed by the particle. Lead absorbers then determined the energy of the particle by restricting the passage of the cosmic ray to trays of counters mounted below the absorber plates

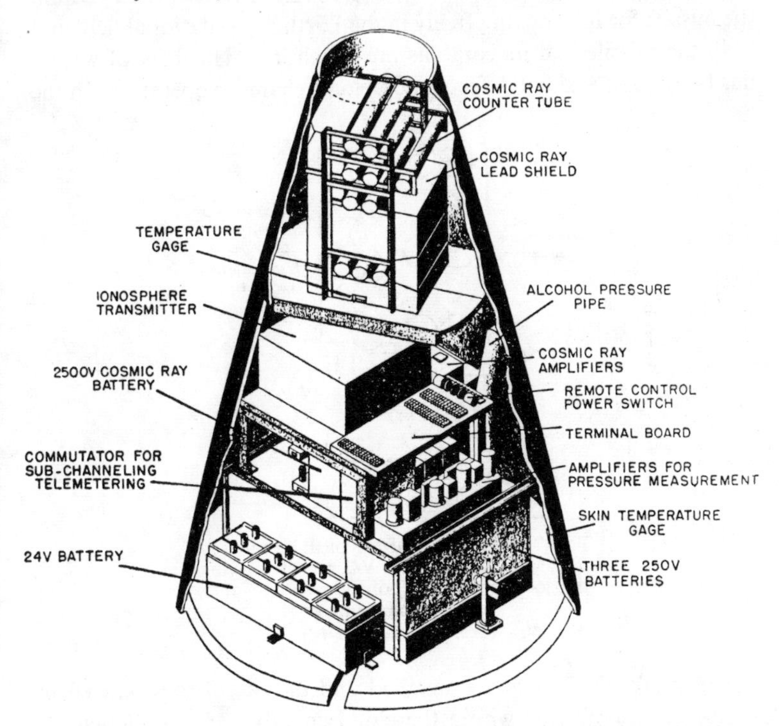

FIG. 7.1—Early V-2 warhead instrumentation showing the location of the cosmic-ray telescope, batteries and amplifiers.
(Courtesy, Naval Research Laboratory)

(Fig. 7.2). If these counters discharged at the same time as the telescope counters, the one cosmic ray would be identified as having passed through certain thicknesses of lead so that its energy could be calculated. Anti-coincidence counters were also arranged around the telescope in order to differentiate between 'real' and 'spurious' rays, that is from showers produced in the structure of the rocket itself; an effect which proved troublesome in the early work when the fairly thick steel warheads were used. A typical warhead instrumentation of a cosmic-ray telescope for a Viking is shown in Fig. 7.3.

Attempts have also been made to fly cloud chambers[7] the first being in 1948.[8, 9] When the propellents of the rocket have been consumed the missile is in a state of free fall. There is no effective gravity within the missile for it is moving freely in the Earth's gravitational field and both the missile and its contents are weightless. This lack of weight has both good and bad effects upon cloud-chamber operation. In the

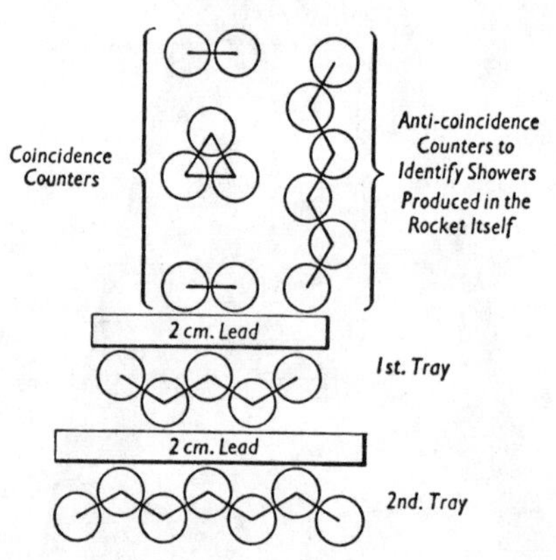

FIG. 7.2—Diagram of a typical cosmic-ray telescope as flown in a V-2 rocket showing the location of the coincidence and anti-coincidence counters.
(*Courtesy, 'The Engineer'*)

first instance the tracks are steadied and the waviness produced by temperature gradients within the cloud chamber are eliminated. At the same time, however, the absence of convection prevents the efficient removal of the condensation nuclei after the expansion and thus gives rise to a building up of background fog which can prevent the recognition of any but the stronger tracks after a few expansions.

Centrifugal force was used to simulate gravity. In the V-2 the effect was obtained by offsetting the cloud chamber in its mounting in quadrant number one of the control chamber aft of the warhead. An attempt was then made to spin the rocket after all-burnt. However, later instrumentations used smaller cloud chambers which were designed to take advantage of the lack of effective gravity and then later to spin the chamber after each expansion in order to clear the fog.

The first cloud chamber used in a V-2 rocket consisted of a glass

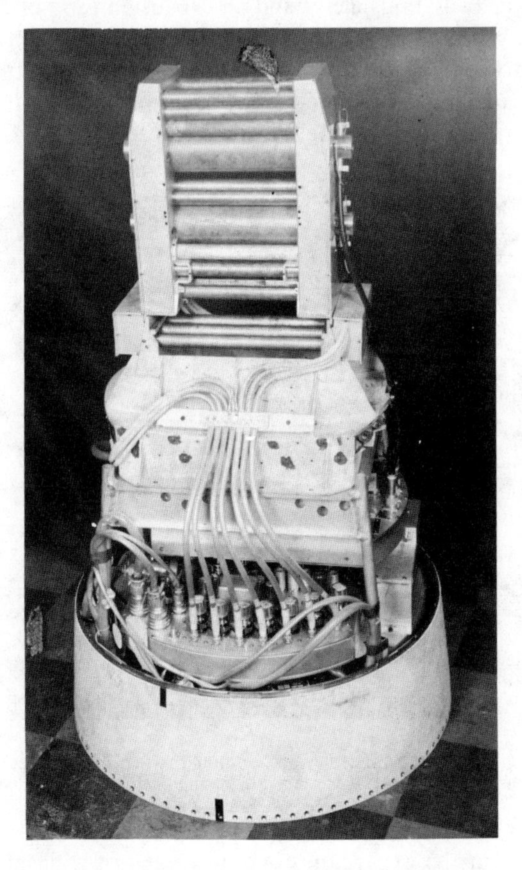

FIG. 7.3—Cosmic-ray telescope mounted in the nose-cone for a Viking rocket.
(Photo., Naval Research Laboratory, Courtesy, 'The Engineer')

cylinder closed by a plate-glass top and a base made from a rubber diaphragm. Inside the chamber an aluminium plate was cemented to the diaphragm and was covered with dark cloth to improve the photographic resolution. Two parallel lead plates, each 1 cm. in thickness, divided the chamber into three equal parts. The complete chamber was 6 inches (15·2 cm.) in diameter and 3 inches (7·6 cm.) in length. The gas used inside the chamber was argon saturated with a mixture of the vapours of ethyl alcohol and water. The internal pressure was two atmospheres and an expansion ratio of about 1·07 was employed. Power for the expansions was derived from compressed nitrogen stored in a cylinder at a pressure of 150 atmospheres. Stereophotographs were obtained by means of a mirror and a modified 35-mm. camera operating without a shutter (Fig. 7.4), exposures

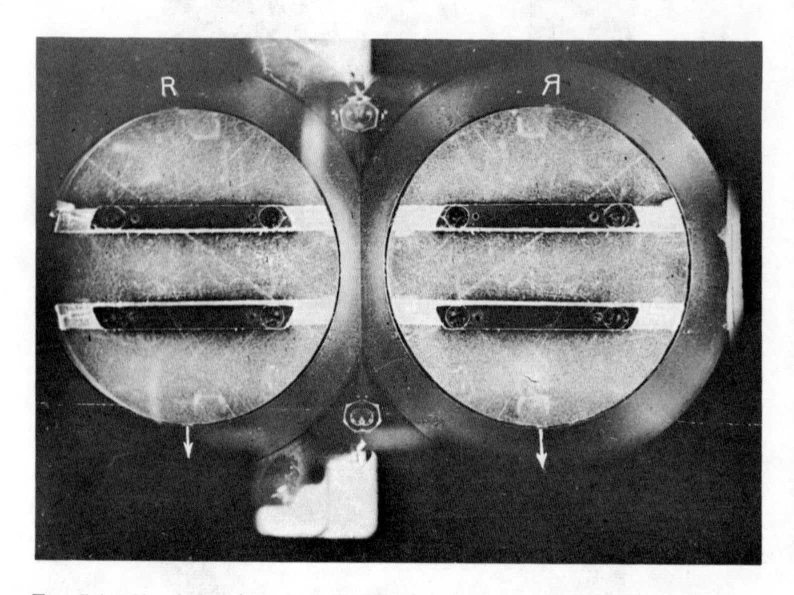

FIG. 7.4—Cloud chamber photographs obtained with a V-2 rocket showing the passage of a cosmic-ray primary above the appreciable atmosphere.
(*Photo., Naval Research Laboratory*)

being made in the expansion cycle by means of a flashing of two lamps mounted in series. The chamber was expanded at twenty-five-second intervals by means of the cosmic-ray electronics, so that about fourteen or fifteen exposures could be made while the rocket was above the appreciable atmosphere. Some good photographs of cosmic-ray primary tracks were obtained.

Single Geiger counters have also been flown and gradually a large amount of data has been gathered.[10, 11, 12] It has been found that particles are knocked up from the top of the atmosphere so that an albedo is detected above certain heights. Gamma radiation has been measured both with Skyhook balloon instrumentations[13] and with equipment carried in V-2 and Aerobee rockets.[14] It has been ascertained that there is no diurnal variation in the intensity of this radiation.

The results of a series of flights of V-2 and Aerobee rockets to 1949[15] in which both single counters and telescopes were flown gave the intensity of cosmic radiation averaged over the whole hemisphere

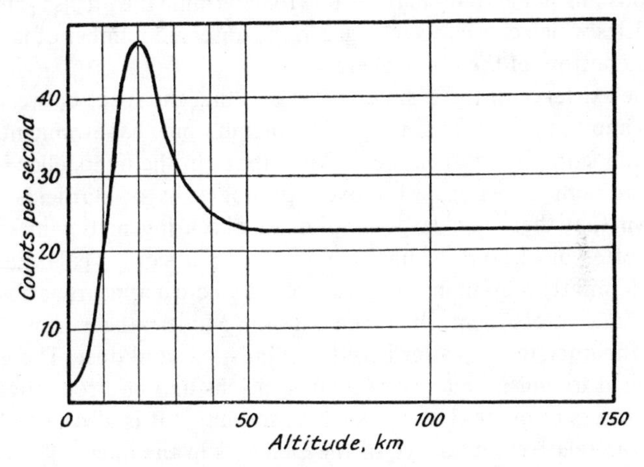

FIG. 7.5—Counts of cosmic rays against altitude as found from a number of experiments with rocket-borne counters.
(After Applied Physics Laboratory, Johns Hopkins University[5])
Single counters flown in V-2, 29th July, 1947, V-2, 27th May, 1948, Aerobee, 5th March, 1948 at geomagnetic latitude 41° N.

as 0·12 particles/cm.²/sec. steradian. It was found also that this remained constant from 34 miles (55 km.) to the highest peak of the flights, namely 100·5 miles (161 km.). The results of a larger number of rocket experiments have been summarized by Van Allen[16] and others[17] and it has been found that there are 0·07 particles/cm.²/sec. steradian in a near vertical direction, 83 per cent being protons, 15·7 per cent being helium nuclei (alpha particles), 1·3 per cent being nuclei of atoms heavier than helium. These figures apply to mid-latitudes. For equatorial regions the intensities are only one-third while in polar regions the number of particles increases threefold.

The biological effects of the cosmic-ray primaries have been discussed by Schaefer[4] and Shepherd[18] and it is concluded that the hazards are not serious just above the atmosphere, but that at great distances from the Earth, where the shielding effects of the planet's field and mass are absent, the dosage may exceed the level of tolerance.

A daily variation in the meson intensity which has been recorded at low altitudes indicates that the Sun may be emitting cosmic rays, and rockets sent to the upper regions of the atmosphere at different periods of solar activity may be able to determine the precise primary particles which cause this increase in the observed number of mesons at the bottom of the atmosphere.

The existence of the cosmic rays shows that the space between the stars and the planets is not a perfect vacuum but that atomic nuclei, possibly complete atoms, are moving about in the interstellar space and at high velocities. Moreover, photographs of starfields have shown that there is a large amount of obscuring matter in space. This often blocks out the light from distant parts of the galaxy and is even similarly present in distant universes where it appears as absorbing bands across them when seen edge on. Modern theory postulates that the interstellar matter is of two kinds, gas and dust. The gas is assumed to consist mainly of hydrogen ions and electrons together with traces of other elements such as sodium.[19] It is also postulated that the relative abundance of the elements in the interstellar gas is in the same order of magnitude as that in the stars and the cosmic rays. The true nature of the dust, on the other hand, is somewhat in doubt. It is found that light from some stars is polarized and it is thought that this polarization is produced by the action of the interstellar dust on the light waves coming to Earth from these stars. Various theories have been put forward in an attempt to explain how the dust creates this polarization; for example, it has been suggested that the dust consists of ferromagnetic material[20] which is aligned in space by magnetic fields or by a collision process with the interstellar gas.[21] Another theory suggests that the grains of interstellar dust consist principally of ice in which the electric dipole of the water molecule causes the crystals, under the influence of an electric field, to grow in such a manner that they will polarize light.[22]

Although the interstellar material may be impinging on the outer layers of the Earth's atmosphere and account for the sodium lines of the night airglow and for the luminous bands in the night sky, its main interest lies in its relation to the interplanetary material in the solar system. Knowledge of the interstellar material is important also for a proper understanding of the growth of stars and, indeed, of the galaxies themselves.

We shall obtain an idea of the scale of the solar system in the next chapter when deep-space probe rockets are discussed. The planets are separated by tremendous distances according to terrestrial standards but the space between them is quite crowded with matter, meteors, cosmic rays, dust, and, it is believed, a certain amount of the interstellar gas. Once again the gas, which might now be termed interplanetary gas, is mainly of ionized hydrogen and free electrons. For the dust, most of the finer particles will be blown out of the solar system by radiation pressure leaving only those particles larger than molecules.

It is believed that we are observing the interplanetary dust when we look at such phenomena as the Zodiacal Light and the Gegenschein, or Counter Glow.

The Zodiacal Light appears as a reddish-yellow or pale white glow which extends from the horizon as a conical shape appearing after twilight and just before dawn. In northern latitudes it is most easily observed in the spring evenings when the ecliptic—plane of the Earth's orbit around the Sun—mounts almost vertically from the horizon, although the axis of the zodiacal cone does not coincide exactly with the plane of the ecliptic. Usually the cone is about the same intensity as the Milky Way in brightness but sometimes it may appear twice as bright.

Then there is a faint glimmer of light in a fairly narrow band which can be traced as an extension of the Zodiacal Light round the celestial sphere to the opposite horizon. It is known as the Zodiacal Band and is very much fainter than the Milky Way; so much so that it is only observable under exceptional conditions on perfectly clear dark nights. Opposite to the Sun, the Zodiacal Band expands into an oval patch of light which appears as a brightening of the band or sometimes as a patch without the band. This is known as the Counter Glow or Gegenschein.

Two possibilities have been suggested to explain these glows. One assumes that they are produced by sunlight reflected from particles in the Earth's exosphere, from a cloud of particles of dust taking a lens shape. The other theory postulates that the particles belong to the Sun and are present in the form of a lens-shaped structure, which reaches out beyond the orbit of the Earth. In this theory the lens-shape accounts for the cone and band while the full phase of the particles beyond the Earth gives rise to the Gegenschein.

In fact it may be that both suggestions will have to be used to account for all the characteristics of the glows.

The spectrum of the Zodiacal Light according to Mitra shows lines and bands similar to the night airglow, together with a continuous solar-type background. This could only be accounted for by reflection of solar light with an added contribution from the excitation of the exosphere. On the other hand no parallax has been observed in the Zodiacal Light, which would appear to indicate that it is remote from the Earth. Soviet astronomers, however, have claimed[23] that they have detected a parallax in the Gegenschein which places it at a distance of twenty Earth radii. It may be that the Gegenschein is thus caused by particles occupying the outer Lagrangian equilibrium point beyond the Earth, otherwise it would be difficult to account for it showing such a small area if it were produced by full and gibbous illumination of an even cloud of particles existing beyond the Earth's orbit.

Fessenkov has suggested that the Earth may, in fact, have a cometary-like tail, blown off from the exosphere, presumably by radiation from the Sun, and that it may be this tail which gives rise to the Gegenschein and to a fainter, false Zodiacal Light which appears as the Gegenschein sinks towards the horizon before dawn, connecting the Counter Glow with the horizon.

There is yet another feature of these faint sky lights which are observable from Earth and which appear somehow to be connected with the Sun. It is known as the Polar Glow, and consists of a segmented area of brightness which is usually observed in midsummer in northern latitudes over the north point at midnight. It would seem to be a part of the Zodiacal Light above the plane of the ecliptic.

When the Sun is eclipsed by the Moon, one of the most striking effects is the appearance of the solar corona, which sometimes spreads out in great pearly equatorial wings with polar tufts at sunspot minimum, while it assumes a quadrilateral form at times of sunspot maximum. The corona is conveniently divided into two regions, the inner or K corona which seems to consist of electrons and ions and which exhibits a continuous spectrum, and the outer or F corona.

Some of the light from the inner corona arises from the photospheric radiations which are scattered by the free electrons. It shows wide Fraunhofer absorption lines which are very much blurred, presumably by Doppler effect due to the high speeds of the electrons. This inner corona is pale yellow in colour and it extends outwards from the limb of the Sun to a distance of about 250,000 miles (400,000 km.).

The wings which stretch out beyond are the F corona and are thought to be visible by light scattered from the interplanetary dust particles.[24] The light shows polarization and also clear Fraunhofer lines which indicate reflected photospheric light. It is nowadays thought that the solar F corona merges into and becomes the Zodiacal Light, but this can only be tested when instruments can be carried to make the necessary measurements beyond the airglow of the atmosphere. Singer has suggested that a coronograph mounted on a Sunseeker instrumentation should be used to make a test of this nature and trace the corona to some 30 or 40 degrees from the Sun. It should then be possible to prove whether or not it does gradually merge into the Zodiacal Light.

Although normal meteors are not so prevalent as to endanger, say, an instrumented Earth satellite vehicle[25, 26, 27] it would appear from these observations that the presence of micrometeorites in the form of the interplanetary dust might become a serious problem for any vehicle which was in space for a considerable time, especially as the concentration of particles appears to lie in the plane of the planetary orbits. Some tests have, indeed, already been made to determine the distribution of the micrometeorites. Highly polished panels of metal have been incorporated in the skins of V-2 rockets. After recovery, microscopic examination showed evidence of pitting which was attributed to the action of the interplanetary dust particles. An electronic instrumentation has also been flown.[28] Skin microphones were used in conjunction with special filter circuits which were designed to register and telemeter impacts which could be attributed to micrometeorites. They counted many impacts. This type of experiment could usefully be carried out to higher altitudes in order to obtain a more accurate idea of the distribution of particles in the vicinity of the Earth. Moreover, a multi-step space probe type of rocket might be fired through the Gegenschein carrying this arrangement of meteor-detecting equipment. A sudden increase in impact rate at the outer Lagrangian equilibrium point would indicate that the Counter Glow is indeed caused by a concentration of micrometeorites in that region rather than by an overall lens-shaped structure extending beyond the terrestrial orbit.

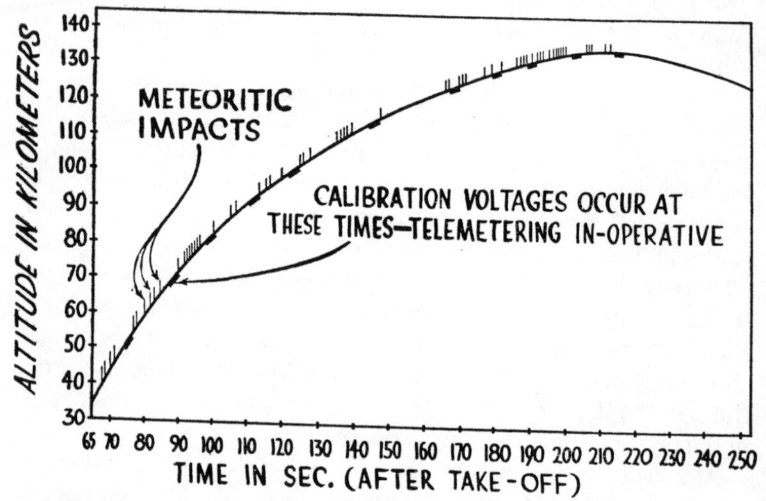

FIG. 7.6—Possible meteoritic impacts with altitude as recorded by sensitive microphones mounted in the modified V-2, No. 31, Blossom 1VD, launched 8th December, 1949.

(*Courtesy, United States Air Force*[28])

Multi-step rockets will be needed for many of the observations concerning the interplanetary matter, but these may not be long delayed providing sufficient funds can be made available. Such vehicles will become invaluable tools for astronomical and astrophysical research outside the exosphere, beyond the frontier to interplanetary space.

REFERENCES

[1] FREIR, P., LOFGREN, E. J., OPPENHEIMER, F., *Physical Review*, **74**, 1818, 1948
[2] BRADT, H. L., PETERS, B., *Physical Review*, **77**, 54, 1950
[3] HARRISON BROWN, *Reviews Modern Phys.*, **21**, 625, 1949
[4] SCHAEFER, H. J., *Jnl. Americ. Rocket Soc.*, **22**, 277, 1952
[5] FRAZER, L. W., *Bumblebee Report* 153, APL, J.H.U., 1951

[6] *Naval Research Laboratory Report* R-2955, Upper Atmosphere Report No. 1, 1946
[7] PERLOW, G. J., *Scientific Monthly*, **69**, 382, 1949
[8] *Naval Research Laboratory Report* R-3120, Upper Atmosphere Report No. 3, 1947
[9] *Naval Research Laboratory Report* R-3358, Upper Atmosphere Report No. 5, 1948
[10] VAN ALLEN, J. A., *Physical Review*, **84**, 791, 1951
[11] GOLIAN, S. E., PERLOW, G. J., KRAUSE, E. H., *Physical Review*, **70**, 223, 1946, **70**, 776, 1946
[12] PERLOW, G. J., *et al.*, *Physical Review*, **88**, 321, 1952
[13] BERGSTRAHL, T. A., SCHROEDER, C. A., *Physical Review*, **81**, 244, 1951
[14] PERLOW, G. J., KISSINGER, C. W., *Physical Review*, **81**, 552, 1951, **84**, 572, 1951
[15] GANGNES, A. V., JENKINS, J. F., VAN ALLEN, J. A., *Physical Review*, **75**, 57, 1949
[16] VAN ALLEN, J. A., loc cit., 10
[17] PERLOW, G. J., *et al.*, loc. cit., 12
[18] SHEPHERD, L. R., *Jnl. Brit. Interpl. Soc.*, **12**, 197, 1953
[19] SEATON, M. J., *Monthly Notices Roy. Astron. Soc.*, **111**, 368, 1951
[20] SPITZER, L., Jr., TUKEY, J. W., *Astrophysical Journal*, **114**, 187, 1951
[21] GOLD, T., *Monthly Notices, Roy. Astron. Soc.*, **112**, 215, 1952
[22] KAHN, F. D., *Monthly Notices, Roy. Astron. Soc.*, **112**, 518, 1952
[23] FASENKOV, V. G., ASTOPOVICH, I. S., DIVARI, N. B., (A), *Nature*, **171**, 555, 1953
[24] VAN DE HULST, H. C., *Astrophysical Journal*, **105**, 471, 1947
[25] OVENDEN, M. W., *Jnl. Brit. Interpl. Soc.*, **6**, 157, 1947
[26] GRIMMINGER, G., *Jnl. Applied Physics*, **19**, 947, 1948
[27] OVENDEN, M. W., *Jnl. Brit. Interpl. Soc.*, **10**, 275, 1951
[28] DUBIN, M., Meteor Impacts by Acoustical Techniques, *Proc. Gassiot Comm.* Oxford, 1953

Chapter Eight

BEYOND THE EXOSPHERE

⪢ ⫴ ⪡

It has been shown that one of the serious limitations of rocket research in the upper atmosphere, especially in so far as astrophysics is concerned, is the short time of stay of the rocket at extreme altitudes. One way of overcoming this difficulty and, indeed, the only one which can be envisaged at the present time, is to place a vehicle into what is termed a satellite orbit.

A body revolving round the Earth in a closed orbit beyond the atmosphere would appear to be capable of continuing its motion indefinitely without the expenditure of energy. Theoretically it is possible for bodies to follow an infinite number of orbits of this type and there may, indeed, be several small natural satellites of this Earth, captured meteors, for example, as well as the Moon. It has been postulated that artificial satellites of this planet could be established and diverse proposals have been put forward to this end. Many of these have been extremely ambitious and verging on the impractical, but there have, on the other hand, been suggestions for small instrumented vehicles which do need serious consideration.

There appears to be no doubt concerning the uses of the artificial satellite for an extension of the high-altitude research programme. Further work could be done on cosmic radiation, ionospheric radio transmission, solar spectra, terrestrial albedo, and possibly on planetary spectra. Before one can decide whether or not such schemes are fanciful it is necessary to examine the fundamental theory of the satellite vehicle and then discuss the engineering problems involved.

The idea of a man-made object eternally pursuing its path through space without the expenditure of energy appears to strike at the roots of classical mechanics with their teachings of the impossibility of perpetual motion. That such a body can exist, however, is daily demonstrated by the revolution of the heavenly bodies, the planets around the Sun, and the satellites around the planets. Everyone is, indeed, familiar with the fact that matter, once in motion, tends to keep that motion unless something obstructs it. Strictly speaking, however, modern theory postulates that the unrestricted motion of a body is only in a straight line when that object is isolated in space. In the presence of matter, such as the Earth or the Sun, the geometry of space is not the simple Euclidean type, but is modified so that the path of a freely moving body becomes a curve. Through a gravitational field, the path of a body may be in the form of an ellipse, parabola, or hyperbola.

Hence, away from matter, energy has to be expended to cause a freely moving body to follow a curved path, whereas near to matter, energy is required to cause the body to move in a straight line. Thus in the case of a tiny body moving in space near to a relatively large mass, the path of the body will be curved and the velocity may be such, that is less than parabolic, that the orbit is closed in on itself and becomes an ellipse. The body should pursue this orbit naturally and without changing from it. In point of fact this is again not strictly true if relativity effects are taken into consideration, for the orbit does not become a closed curve. The resultant modifications to the orbit can be regarded in such a manner that the normal ellipse which should result is perturbed and there is a revolution of the major axis in the plane of the ellipse so that the positions of perihelion and aphelion advance. This effect is only appreciable with fast-moving objects close to large masses, and in the solar system it reaches a measurable amount in the case of the planet Mercury which is the closest planet to the Sun.

Basically, therefore, for most purposes, the heavenly bodies can be regarded as moving in ellipses, except that they perturb each other and slightly modify their respective orbits. There are also braking effects caused by tidal friction and impacts with the dust and the débris which litter space. Movement through a retarding medium decreases the radius vector, which is defined as the line joining the moving body to the centre of attraction. This results in an increase of the linear velocity at all points in the orbit, with a consequent reduction in the period of revolution. Although this may, at first, seem to be paradoxical, it can be explained that the resistance to the motion of the body causes it to fall towards the centre of attraction. The result is a gain in kinetic energy at the expense of potential energy and the body moves in an orbit closer to the centre of attraction. It must there move faster in order to maintain its orbit.

We have seen that there is a great amount of débris in space in the form of interplanetary gas and meteors, ranging in size from particles smaller than molecules to huge masses of many tons. However, the effect of such braking on the planets of the solar system is negligible, except when considered over periods of millions of years. Man-made bodies, travelling through space, would similarly be unaffected unless there was an individual contact between the space rocket and a meteor. Statistical analyses[1, 2] show that such an eventuality must be extremely rare and that a small instrumented satellite would have a good chance of surviving many years.

It is thus possible to consider a body which is already in space at some finite distance away from the Earth and which, once it has been set in motion, will continue to move through this unrestricting medium beyond the exosphere. There can be ascertained the velocity which must be imparted to the body so that it will move in a circular orbit around the Earth.

The simplest case of an orbiting body is thus one in which the path is circular. The velocity needed to maintain the orbit can be calculated by equating the gravitational force at the radius of the orbit to the centrifugal force, namely,

$$V = \sqrt{g_0 \,.\, R^2/r}$$

where g_0 is the acceleration of gravity at the surface of the Earth, R is the radius of the Earth and r is the radius of the circular orbit. The period of a body moving in such an orbit is readily obtainable from:

$$T = \frac{2 \,.\, \pi}{R}\sqrt{\frac{r^3}{g_0}}$$

and it will probably be advantageous to have this some convenient fraction of the period of rotation of the Earth in order to facilitate tracking.

The total energy of a body in the orbit is given by the sum of the potential and kinetic energies, that is,

$$E = \frac{g_0 \,.\, R}{2r}\,(2r - R)$$

A body revolving at, say, 200 miles (322 km.) would thus have an energy of $3{\cdot}3 \times 10^7$ kg.m/kg. whereas one in the 24-hour orbit would have an energy of $5{\cdot}8 \times 10^7$ kg.m/kg.

It can be shown that the velocity needed for a body to proceed in a circular orbit at any level in a gravitational field is equal to 0·707 times the escape velocity at that level. This velocity must, of course, be applied in a direction at right angles to the radius vector. Thus a body revolving at the limits of the atmosphere of the Earth would have to move at a speed of 4·9 miles per second (7·9 km./sec.), whereas at the distance of the Moon this speed reduces to 0·6 miles per second (1·03 km./sec.) being, indeed, that at which the Moon travels along its orbit.

At first sight it would seem, therefore, that it may be much easier to accelerate a rocket projectile to the circular velocity than it would be to cause it to overcome the Earth's field in a parabolic orbit, for circular velocity is always less than three-quarters of the value of parabolic escape velocity. While this may be so, it is also necessary to raise the rocket some distance above the surface of the Earth to clear the atmosphere. A simple analysis will show that it is not possible to shoot a missile from the surface of the Earth into a closed orbit. All such missiles must follow paths which cut the surface of the Earth at two points, at take-off and at impact. In order to establish the circulating body it is necessary to apply a propulsive force at two separate stages.

Two extremes exist for the establishment of a missile in a circular orbit, these being illustrated in Fig. 8.1. First there is the 'A' type orbit which, in the limit, means ascending vertically along the radius vector to the distance of the chosen circular orbit, then applying a velocity at right angles thus attaining orbital velocity. The curve of the 'A' orbit graph shows how wasteful of energy this procedure is. The other extreme, which produces optimum conditions, is to accelerate the rocket horizontally from launching to perigee velocity of orbit 'C', which is an ellipse touching the Earth's surface at perigee and the circular orbit at apogee. A further velocity increment is added when the rocket has travelled along the elliptical transfer orbit to the position of apogee and at that point transfer is then made to the required circular orbit. It is apparent from the figure that the velocity increments of a type 'C' ascent are much less than the requirements for a type 'A' vertical ascent. Even so, under optimum conditions, slightly more energy is needed to establish certain circular orbits than is required to escape completely on a parabolic orbit. Such orbits are all at distances greater than about three and a half Earth radii.

From the figure it can thus be seen that the total velocity change

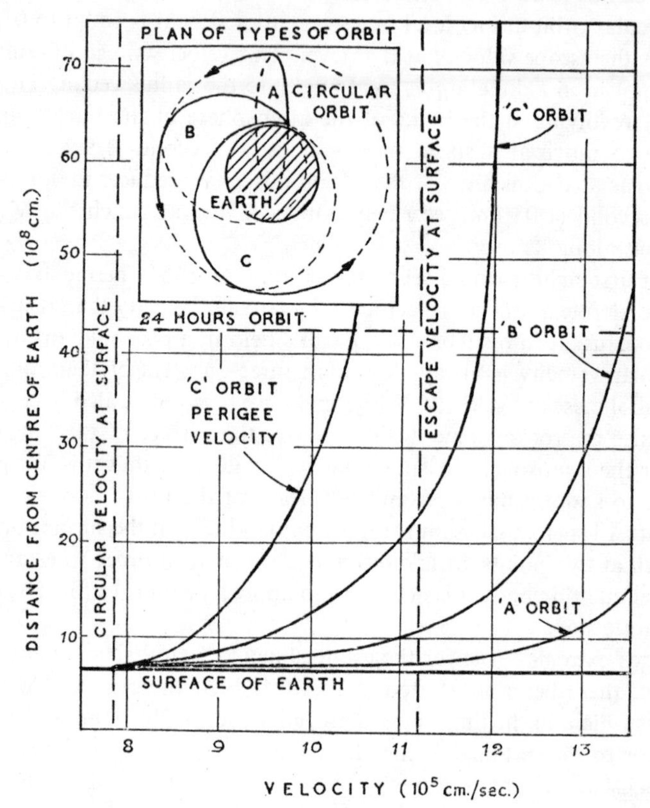

FIG. 8.1—The optimum path for establishing a rocket in a circular orbit is a type C transfer ellipse which grazes the surface of the Earth and the circular orbit. This figure shows the total velocity required to establish a rocket in a circular orbit at a determined distance from the Earth using various types of transfer orbits. (*Courtesy, 'Aeronautics'*)

required (characteristic velocity) to place the rocket into the circular orbit is only appreciably less than that of escape when the circular orbit is close to the surface of the planet. This results from the need for two separate periods of power which necessitates lifting propellents through the gravitational potential for use at apogee.

The closest orbits, just beyond the atmosphere, need a characteristic velocity of nearly 6·2 miles per second (10 km./sec.), which should be compared with 1·5 miles per second (2·5 km./sec.) attained by a modern rocket such as the two-step Bumper-WAC. As will later be shown, it appears feasible that the necessary increase in all-burnt velocities can be made and the orbital body accordingly placed in position. Artificial moons of this nature, once they are established, will have perturbed orbits like those of any other celestial body. If these satellites are to be considered as practical propositions it must be determined whether or not their orbits will be stable, or if the various perturbations will cause them to be so modified that the artificial satellite will be destroyed.

First perturbation will be caused by the Sun which will have the effect of pulling the satellite away from the Earth at conjunction and opposition (the syzygies, when the Sun, Earth and satellite are in the same straight line) and towards the Earth at the positions of quadrature. This is analogous to the tide-raising force so far as the action of the various accelerations which are involved is concerned.

There are also perturbations resulting from the equatorial bulge of the Earth, especially if the satellite is a close one. If the orbit is inclined to the equatorial plane, the nodes will regress. The action of the Sun also causes the nodes to regress upon a proper plane which is a sort of compromise between the plane of the ecliptic and the plane of the Earth's equator (Fig. 8.2). With an elliptical orbit the equatorial bulge also produces an advance in the lines of apsides so causing the geocentric longitude of the perigee and apogee to change.

The presence of the comparatively close and massive Moon will considerably modify the orbit of an artificial satellite, but only in certain cases can the perturbations became destructive. If the plane of the satellite orbit differs from the plane of the lunar orbit, the action of the Moon will be to produce changes in the eccentricity and inclination and even of the periodic time of the orbit of the artificial satellite. The changes will depend upon the position of the geocentric conjunction and opposition relative to the lines of the nodes and apses. If the motion of these lines is neglected, the perturbations would strictly only be periodic if the periods of revolution of the Moon and the artificial satellite were commensurable: for example, one-half, one-third, two-fifths, one-quarter, &c., of the lunar period. In such cases the perturbations would tend to reinforce each other at successive revolutions ultimately reaching large, even destructive, values. However, if the periodic times are only nearly equal, inequalities of long period would be set up and these

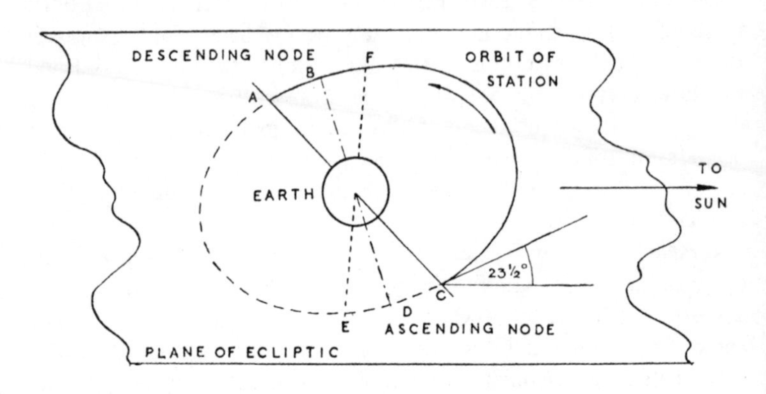

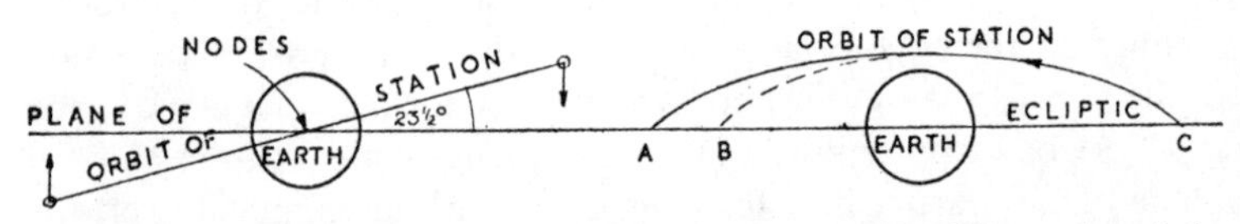

FIG. 8.2—The effect of the Sun is to produce a regression of the nodes of the satellite orbit. Ascending above the plane of the ecliptic at *C*, the satellite is encouraged to return to that plane sooner than it would do if the Sun were not attracting it. The descending node thus becomes *B* instead of *A*. Similarly when beneath the ecliptic, the satellite is urged back again so that the node moves from *D* to *E*. Over a long period of time the orbit thus appears to wobble, the pole of the orbit describing a circle of radius 23½° around the pole of the ecliptic. A similar effect on the equatorial bulge of the Earth causes the Earth's axis to wobble once in every 25,800 years.

(*Courtesy*, '*Aeronautics*')

could only become troublesome if the satellite revolved for hundreds of years.

The effects of destructive perturbations of this form are exhibited in nature by the gaps in the rings of the planet Saturn and gaps in the belt of asteroids which swarm around the Sun between the orbits of Mars and Jupiter. The gaps in the rings represent orbits of moonlets which would have periods commensurable with those of satellites of Saturn, whereas the gaps in the asteroids occur at such distances from the Sun that bodies moving in orbits there would have periods commensurable with that of the planet Jupiter.

The Moon will also perturb the artificial satellite as planets of the solar system perturb one another. The radial and orthogonal components of the disturbing force in this case have the effect of altering the period of the satellite and causing rotation of the apse line and regression of the nodes of the satellite orbit. These effects can be

TABLE 8.1 *Perturbations on an Earth-satellite*

Due to the Moon	Direct rotation of the line of apsides Regression of the nodes Variation in the eccentricity of the orbit Change in the periodic time of the orbit
Due to the Sun	Lengthens the period Direct rotation of the line of apsides Accelerates motion at conjunction and opposition and retards motion at the quadratures Deflects circular orbit into an ellipse with major axis at right angles to radius vector from Sun to Earth Causes changes in the eccentricity of elliptical orbit depending upon the position of the apsides, also a variation of the period due to the elliptical orbit of the Earth Inequalities of motion over the whole of the orbit, varying areal velocity, greatest before conjunction least before opposition
Due to the Earth	On elliptical orbit not inclined to the plane of the equator, direct motion of the apsides On inclined elliptical orbit, direct motion of the apsides, regression of the nodes On circular orbit inclined to the equator, regression of the nodes.

investigated by the methods of celestial mechanics which are used to determine the mutual disturbances of the planets of the solar system.

A summary of the various perturbations is given in Table 8.1, and the conclusion arrived at is that a suitable choice of orbit can ensure that disturbances need never be so great as to endanger the stability of the orbit of an artificial satellite but will merely modify its form.

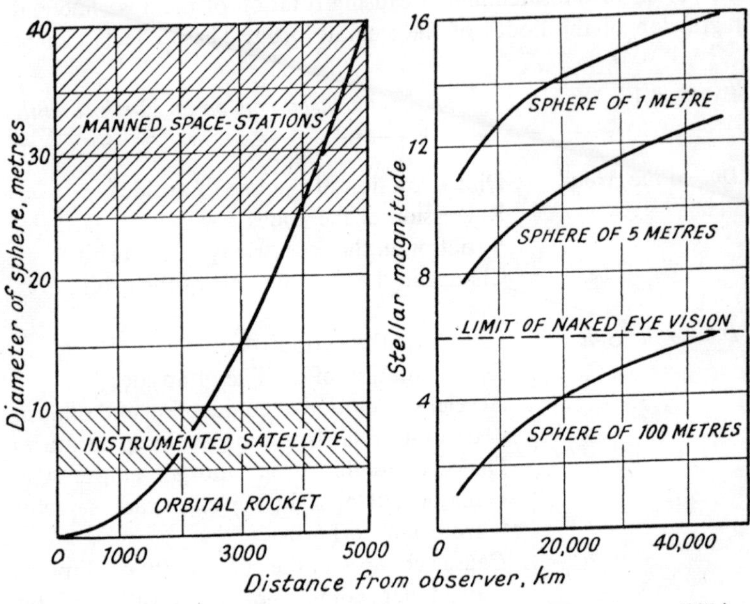

FIG. 8.3—Detection of the artificial satellite. This figure shows the possibilities of detecting the satellite by radar or optically.
(*Courtesy*, '*The Engineer*')

If even a simple uninstrumented satellite could thus be placed in the circular orbit and could be observed from Earth it would prove a useful aid to navigation and could also be used for physical research by radio reflection and observations of its stellar magnitude. The first real use of the artificial satellite may well be in this way.

Two methods of observing the satellite are possible, by radar and optically. If the body of the satellite is assumed to act merely as a passive reflector the results are not very encouraging. A transponder in the missile considerably improves the picture. Assuming that the Earth station has an aerial array 60 square yards (50 sq. metres) in

cooling to take advantages of the highest combustion-chamber temperatures, a specific impulse of 250 seconds will be obtained. The usual propellent determinants for military use such as toxicity, ease of handling, commercial availability, storage, cost, &c., would not be of such importance for a research vehicle.

Finally we should consider the payload of the artificial satellite. The design requirements so far laid down indicate that there will be required 1,000 units of take-off mass for each unit of payload placed into the orbit. This is assuming a payload factor of 0·1; the V-2's was 0·08 and the Viking's 0·17. If we are a little more ambitious and instead of the simple missile we aim at a payload of telemetering instruments and power supplies weighing 200 pounds (90 kg.), the build-up of the orbital rocket would be somewhat along the following lines:

		Tons	
	1st Step	*2nd Step*	*3rd Step*
Payload	8·94	0·894	0·089
Structure	13·4	1·34	0·134
Propellents	67·02	6·70	0·670
Totals	89·36	8·94	0·894

It would not be necessary to develop a new large motor for the first step because four motors of the V-2 type giving a combined thrust of 104 tons, together with a ring of cellular drop boosters would suffice to power it. No unusual structural problems would be presented and pumps capable of delivering the requisite amounts of propellents are available. The second and third steps would be very much the same as rockets already in use today. The really difficult part, however, may be the instrumentation for the control of the rocket and the entry into the correct orbit, but research into the problems of control of guided missiles is continually helping to ease this difficulty.

An early experiment immediately suggests itself. This would be the determination of the characteristics of the exosphere. The payload to be placed into the satellite orbit might consist of an expandable nylon or plastic sphere suitably metallized for radar detection or alternatively containing a transponder. Placed at various heights, spheres such as this would undergo orbital changes due to the action of the exospheric gases and from these changes a calculation could be made concerning the density and the extent of the exosphere. These factors must be accurately known before any instrumented satellite is designed to operate in any orbit fairly close to the Earth.

With an instrumented vehicle power supplies become a problem. A normal high-altitude rocket may carry half of its payload in the form of power supplies which are needed to operate its instruments for just a few minutes. It will be impractical to attempt to power the instrumented satellite from batteries or from the energy of fuel carried up to drive a generator. There remains, however, the possibility of tapping the 'free' energy of the solar system, and the most obvious source is the solar radiations. The system envisaged is a solar engine which would intercept a relatively minute portion of the 92,000 calories which each square centimetre of the Sun's surface radiates every minute. At the mean distance of the Earth from the Sun (150,000,000 km.) this energy is considerably reduced in intensity, but nevertheless it is found that a surface of one square centimetre, on which the Sun's rays fall perpendicularly, intercepts energy at the rate of 2·0 calories per minute. This value is known as the solar constant and it has already been shown how its exact determination has been the result of study by rocket techniques.

It is assumed, therefore, that a suitable mirror is used to focus the rays from the Sun on coils through which circulates a working fluid. If the area of the mirror is 1·2 square yards (1 sq. metre) the heat available will amount to $2{\cdot}0 \times 10^4$ calories per minute, and the First Law of Thermodynamics shows that this has a work rate equivalent to 1·4 kilowatts. The temperature of the working fluid would be determined by the rate of flow and could reach quite high values. The complete power unit of this type is shown in Fig. 8.4. From the heater coils the working fluid expands through a turbine and passes to the low temperature/low pressure side of the closed cycle. Unwanted heat could be rejected into the sink of space by radiators on the shadowed side of the orbital vehicle.

A compressor connected to the turbine shaft would be used to feed the working fluid from the low-pressure back to the high-pressure side of the system. It would be advantageous to use a working substance which has a high specific heat ratio (generally the case with monatomic gases) but also it must have a high density in order to minimize the size of the apparatus both in regard to physical dimensions and the number of stages for the compressor and the turbine. Erosion and chemical deterioration must be avoided if the satellite is to operate for any considerable time and an inert working fluid would hence be preferable. It is possible that the rare gas argon would be the best choice; it has comparatively high density, is inert, and is monatomic. Mercury vapour might also be considered but

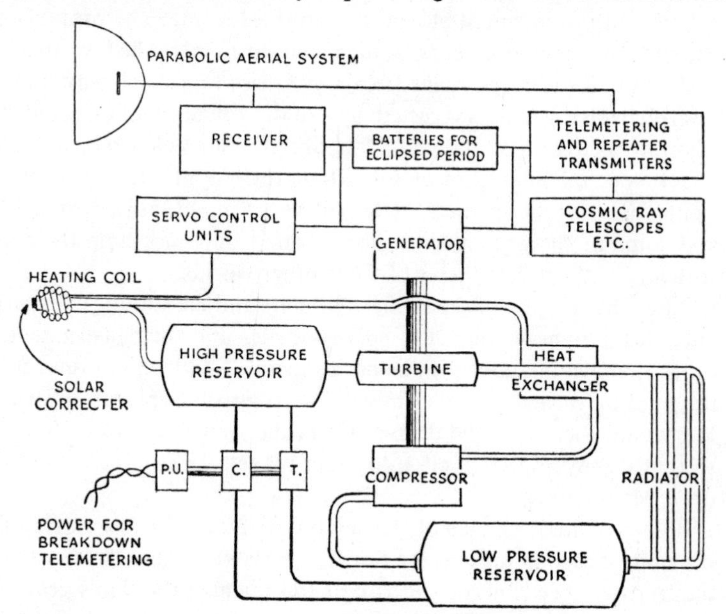

FIG. 8.4—Schematic of power unit and electrical system for an instrumented satellite. Energy is collected from the solar radiation and used to heat a working substance which drives a turbine thus creating electrical power through a generator.

(*Courtesy*, '*Aeronautics*')

the high freezing point (234·1° K. compared with 84° K. for argon) restricts the lower temperature end of the cycle. The power needed to telemeter information to Earth from a vehicle moving at the limits of the atmosphere would have an order of magnitude of only about 100 watts and could be supplied by this type of equipment.

An extension of the high-altitude rocket research programme will be the first use to which an instrumented satellite will be put. Cosmic-ray telescopes and counters and other instruments could be maintained in space for relatively long periods of time. Solar, lunar and terrestrial spectroscopy might be investigated, the magnetic field of the Earth recorded, especially during times of solar storms. Essentially the satellite will be a solar observatory capable of obtaining data concerning the emission of radiation by the Sun at wavelengths far into the ultra-violet region of the spectrum. Solar corpuscles would be recorded in an attempt to find out their nature and their relationship to magnetic storms and to the aurorae. The problem of the sudden commencement of a magnetic storm might be investigated to find out if the corpuscular stream gives rise to a shock wave in the interplanetary gas as suggested by Gold.[3] Some missiles could be instrumented with stable platforms like the Sunseeker which could check spectral intensities at important regions of the spectrum of light from the other planets. Mars and Venus might thus be examined and some of the present difficulties cleared up concerning the constituents of the atmospheres of these other worlds.

After the creation of the artificial satellite and the gaining of experience in the remote control of space vehicles and their instrumentations, there would appear to be no insuperable difficulties preventing the sending of instrumented missiles deep into interplanetary space. We would then have the deep-space probe which could be directed so that it may approach close to other planets or even be caused to orbit Mars or Venus.

Because all the planets of the solar system are already moving in the same direction around the Sun at speeds very much greater than the transfer speeds needed to rise or fall through the Sun's gravitational potential between the planetary orbits, it is found that the paths of transfer are ellipses with the Sun at one of the foci. Moreover, the ellipses for minimum propellent requirements just touch the orbits of the planets of take-off and destination. These are known as tangential transfer ellipses.[4]

Although the planets move in ellipses around the Sun, their orbits are not exactly in the same plane. The orbit of Mars is inclined at an angle of 1·85° to the ecliptic. Arising from the elliptical orbits, the distances of the planets from the Sun vary during the course of their revolutions and their velocities vary throughout the orbits. The Earth is at perihelion about 1st January, being closest to the Sun during winter in the northern hemisphere. It is then some 3,000,000 miles (5,000,000 km.) nearer to the Sun than it is at aphelion. At perihelion, moreover, it travels at a velocity of 18·9 miles per second

(30·25 km./s.) compared with 18·25 miles per second (29·26 km./s.) at the most distant part of its orbit. Mars, on the other hand, reaches perihelion at the part of its orbit compared with the position of the

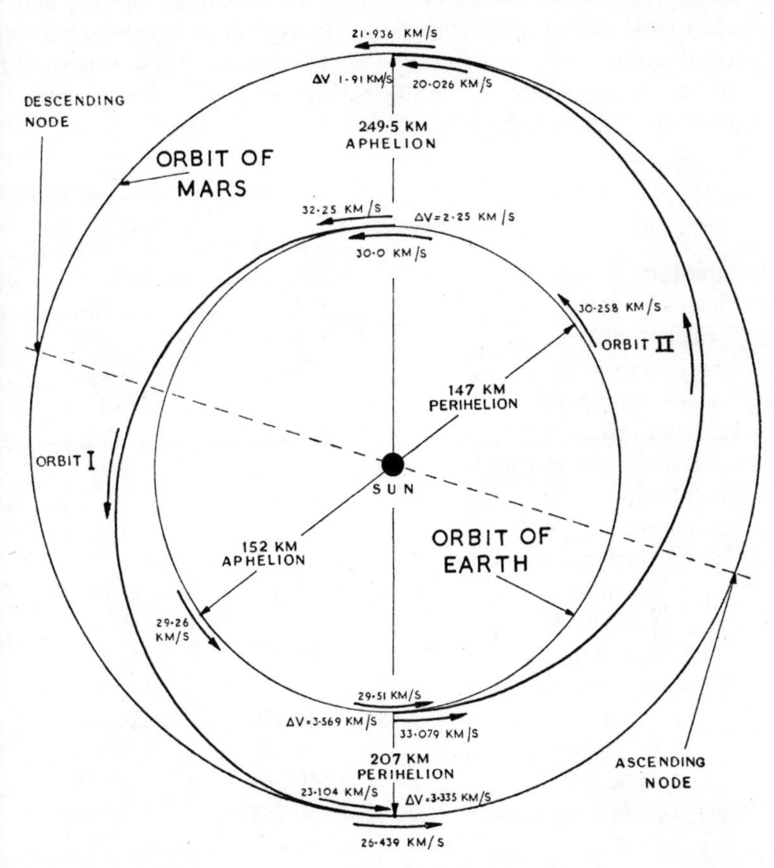

FIG. 8.5—Orbits of the planets Earth and Mars showing the positions of aphelion and perihelion and the orbital velocities at those points. (Distances are given in millions of kilometres.)

(*Courtesy, 'Aeronautics'*)

Earth in late August, at a longitude of 335·1°, which is measured from the position of the Earth at the autumnal equinox (on the radius vector pointing to the first point of Aries). Perihelion and aphelion of Mars do not, therefore, coincide with those of the Earth, neither do they occur in the plane of the Earth's orbit. The ascending node is 49·1° from the autumnal equinox position of the Earth.

These figures enable the two orbits to be compared and make it possible to ascertain when the planets will be closest together and when most distant apart (Fig. 8.5). The type of manœuvre needed to pass from one to the other can then be obtained. These important orbital data are collected in Table 8.3 and data on the planets themselves are given in Table 8.4.

TABLE 8.3 *Orbits of Earth and Mars*

	Earth	*Mars*
Period, days	365	687
Mean distance	1	1·524
Perihelion distance	0·984	1·382
Aphelion distance	1·03	1·667
Perihelion longitude	102·1°	335·1°
Perihelion passage	1st Jan.	late Aug.
Ascending node longitude ..	—	49·1°
Eccentricity	0·01675	0·09326
Inclination	—	1·85°
Orbital velocity miles/sec. ..		
mean	18·5	15·0
perihelion	18·8	16·4
aphelion	18·2	13·6
Orbital velocity km./sec.		
mean	29·759	24·10
perihelion	30·258	26·439
aphelion	29·26	21·936
Solar constant watts/cm.^{2} ..	0·1325	0·0568

Distances are given in astronomical units where one astronomical unit is equal to 93×10^6 miles ($149{\cdot}5 \times 10^6$ km.).

It is known that at escape velocity a body can overcome the gravitational field of the Earth and theoretically travel to infinity. Moreover, if it commences with a higher initial velocity, a hyperbolic one, it should arrive at infinity with some residual velocity. This is the condition to be aimed at with the deep-space probe rocket, remembering that when speaking of infinity we mean in the practical, as

TABLE 8.4 *Planets Earth and Mars*

Radius, mean, km.	6378·388	3392·0
miles	3975	2110
Rotation, hours	24	24·6
Acceleration of gravity, mean, at		
surface, m/s^2	9·80665	3·69
ft/s^2	32·12	11·2
Inclination of equator to orbit ..	23·45°	25·167°
Escape velocity, mean, at surface,		
km./sec.	11·1784	4·999
miles/sec.	6·95	3·1

opposed to the academic, case, a very great distance from the Earth. In effect there must be imparted to the probe missile by its rocket motor such a velocity that, having overcome the gravitational attraction of the Earth, it will have sufficient residual velocity for it to effect

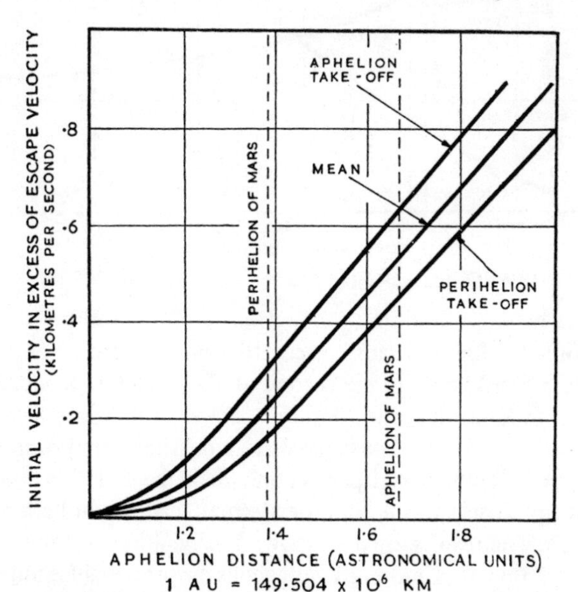

FIG. 8.6—Velocities in excess of escape needed to reach distances from the Sun assuming take-off from Earth at mean, perihelion and aphelion positions.
(*Courtesy*, '*Aeronautics*')

transfer from the Earth's orbit around the Sun to an elliptical orbit which has its aphelion at the distance of the planet Mars. This is the first basic requirement of a planetary probe to Mars. If nothing else were done, telemetering equipment could send data obtained during the resulting close approach to the planet.

It is possible to calculate the excess over escape velocity needed to leave Earth with definite residual velocities. These initial velocities are shown in Fig. 8.6. They represent all-burnt velocities which rockets must attain in order to reach calculated distances from the

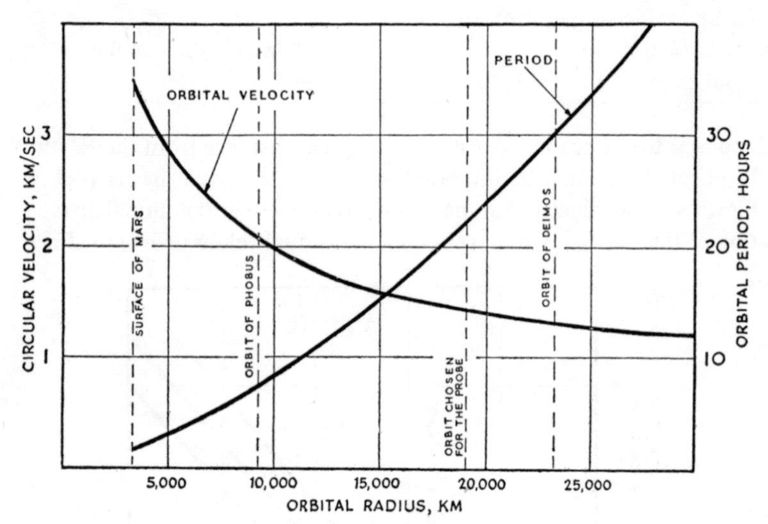

FIG. 8.7—Orbital velocities and periods of satellites of Mars. (*Courtesy, 'Aeronautics'*)

Sun. From this figure it can be seen that an increase of only a few hundredths of a kilometre per second at all-burnt can produce most impressive final results.

There are two extremes possible when a missile is fired from Earth. First it can be launched at perihelion, when the Earth is travelling fastest but is closest to the Sun, or alternatively, it can be launched at aphelion. The results are also shown in Fig. 8.6 from which it can be gathered that it is more advantageous in propellent economy if take-off from Earth is made at perihelion. Then it has to be considered which is most economical at the Martian end of the transfer, to approach Mars at aphelion or perihelion?

The results of an analysis[5, 6] show that an approach to Mars at aphelion is preferable. It follows from a general rule[5] that for a journey to any planet with a lesser escape velocity than that of the Earth the greatest orbital transfer velocity, when any choice is possible, should be at the change from Earth's orbit to voyage orbit.

As we have seen, the lines of apsides of the two orbits do not coincide, and a rocket could not be launched along a tangential transfer ellipse to leave Earth at perihelion and reach Mars at its aphelion.

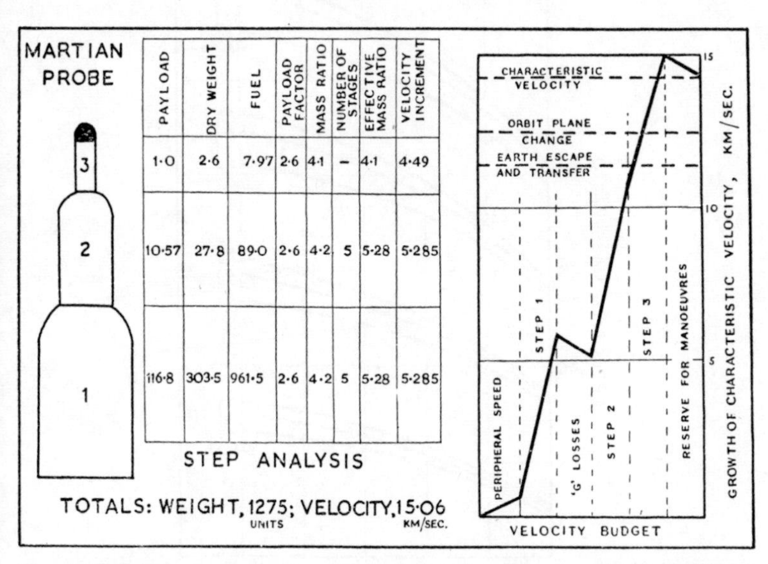

PAYLOAD	DRY WEIGHT	FUEL	PAYLOAD FACTOR	MASS RATIO	NUMBER OF STAGES	EFFECTIVE MASS RATIO	VELOCITY INCREMENT
1·0	2·6	7·97	2·6	4·1	–	4·1	4·49
10·57	27·8	89·0	2·6	4·2	5	5·28	5·285
116·8	303·5	961·5	2·6	4·2	5	5·28	5·285

FIG. 8.8—Requirements for a probe rocket to become an artificial satellite of Mars. For every unit of payload carried, a take-off mass of 1,275 units is required. Expendable construction is assumed for the 1st and 2nd steps of the missile. (*Courtesy*, '*Aeronautics*')

The probe must leave Earth 54 days before perihelion, that is about 26th February. A probe approaching Mars so that it would have escape velocity if it reached the surface of the planet would require a velocity change of 0·4 miles per second (0·64 km./sec.) to enter a circular orbit around Mars with a radius of 11,500 miles (18,500 km.) and a period of 21 hours (Fig. 8.7). It is then found that the characteristic velocity for the mission taking advantage of the best orbit to aphelion, amounts to 8·8 miles per second (14·1 km./sec.). This would tax engineering resources to the practical limits.

At least three steps would appear to be required having mass ratios of 4·2 and developing specific impulses of 325 seconds, and expendable construction would be required with the first and second steps. The layout of the probe rocket would thus be along the lines of Fig. 8.8. It is found that for every unit of payload carried into the satellite orbit around Mars there will be required 1,275 units of take-

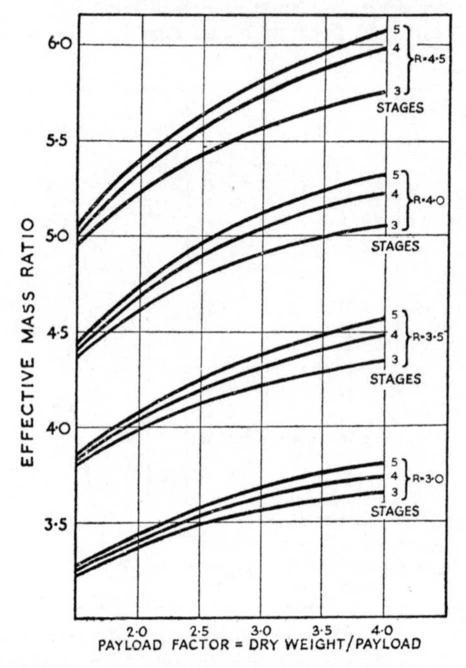

FIG. 8.9—The effective mass ratio obtained by using expendable construction. This figure shows that considerable gains in effective mass ratio are possible with only a few stages of tank jettisoning.
(Courtesy 'Aeronautics')

off mass. The figure also shows the velocity budget and how characteristic velocity would be built up over the various stages, taking into account the main losses.

Essentially the Martian probe would be concerned with five types of measurement. First will be regarding the aspect of the probe itself, for other data will be useless without this knowledge. The orientation of the probe relative to the Sun can be determined by means of photo-cells. The second series of measurements will also be made by photo-cells which will form an optical scanner for building up a detailed picture of the surface of Mars. Thirdly there will be an attempt to measure the magnetic field of the planet and its intensity, then there will be the cosmic-ray counts to determine the effect of the

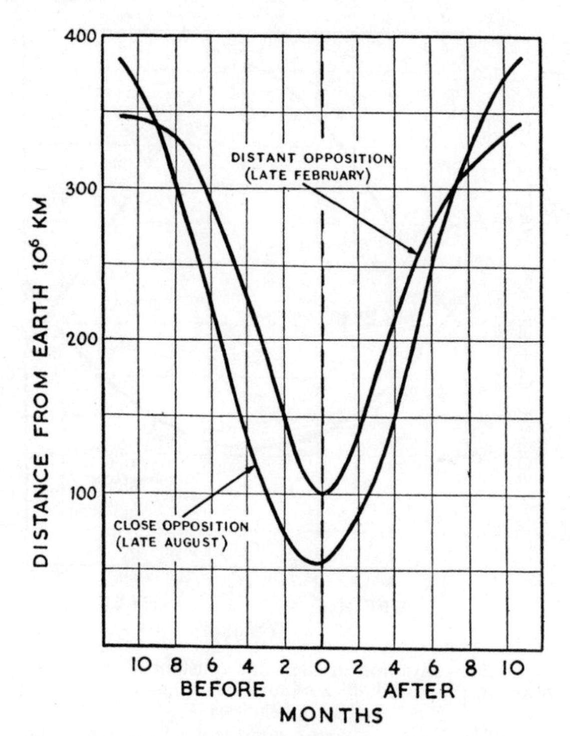

FIG. 8.10—Distances separating Earth and Mars for 11 months before and after both good and bad oppositions.
(*Courtesy*, '*Aeronautics*')

heliocentric field on the primary spectrum. Finally a radar survey of the planet may be made in an attempt to build up a rough contour map.

The next stage is to analyse the requirements for telemetering data from Mars to Earth. Neglecting, for the present, the tremendous variation in distance separating the two planets at opposition and conjunction, it must be realized that all oppositions are not equally favourable. At closest approach, such as will occur in 1956, 1970 and 1985, Mars can come within 35 × 10⁶ miles (56 × 10⁶ km.), whereas at a distant opposition the gulf between the planets becomes 63 × 10⁶ miles (100 × 10⁶ km.). We shall thus require about four times as much transmitted power at a bad opposition as at a good one.

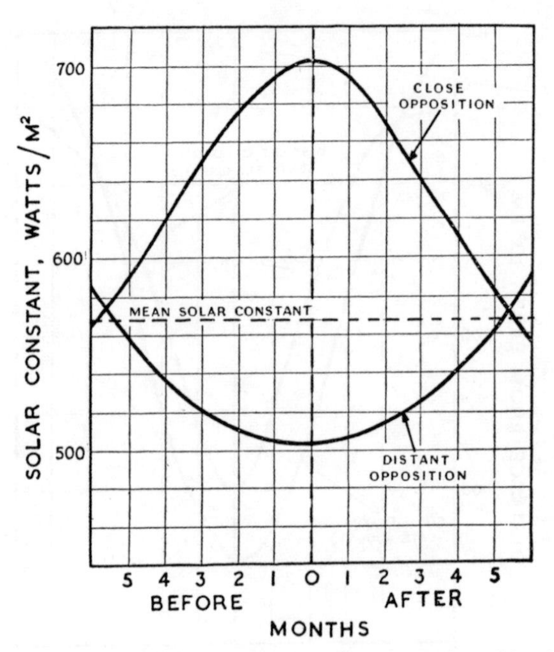

FIG. 8.11—Variation of the solar constant at the orbit of Mars for the period of six months before and after good and bad oppositions.

(Courtesy 'Aeronautics')

Moreover, the distance separating the planets varies quite rapidly both before and after oppositions. This is shown in Fig. 8.10. In Fig. 8.12 is shown the power required for transmitting data, assuming unity at a bad opposition. This power will have to be obtained from a closed-cycle solar-power unit as with the artificial Earth satellite but the solar constant varies quite a lot over the Martian orbit. Fig. 8.11 shows the solar constant at the Martian orbit for six months before and after good and bad extremes of opposition. Taken in conjunction with the previous figure it shows a limitation of the useful period of transmission from the Martian probe. But what amount of power is going to be needed?

First it is assumed that aerial arrays are used and, of course, the

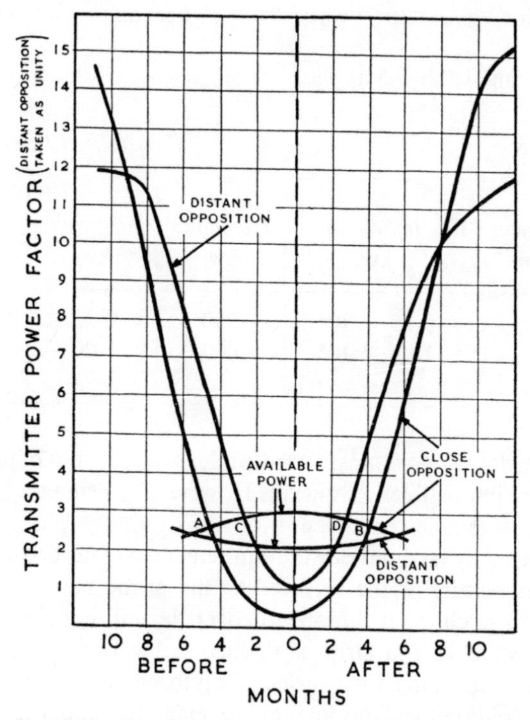

FIG. 8.12—Transmitted power required for the period eleven months before and after good and bad oppositions taking that required at a distant opposition as being unity. The available power for an arbitrary solar engine is indicated taking the variation of the solar constant into account and it shows how time of transmission may be considerably reduced at the period of a bad opposition.

(*Courtesy*, '*Aeronautics*')

largest array will have to be at the Earth-end of the radio link because the probe rocket's size will considerably limit the rocket-borne equipment. In order to arrive at some comparative figures one can assume that the array on the rocket can be one square metre in area while that on Earth is taken as being one hundred times as great.

Assuming that the minimum signal strengths[7] needed for reception are:

Television ..	10^{-9} watts	Telephony ..	10^{-12} watts
Telegraphy ..	10^{-15} watts	A beacon ..	10^{-20} watts

the following Table 8.5 applies.

TABLE 8.5 *Transmitted Power required*

Distance 10^6 *km.*	*television* kw.	*telephony* kw.	*telegraphy* kw.	*beacon* w.
50	$0{\cdot}25 \times 10^6$	250	0·25	0·0025
100	$1{\cdot}00 \times 10^6$	1,000	1·00	0·01

Even at close oppositions, close-up television pictures of the planet's surface are impossible to transmit. However, by using a system similar to the facsimile transmission of news photographs, Cross[8] has shown that only medium power requirements are needed to transmit a scanned picture of the surface. As the probe passes over Mars, taking 6·83 satellite revolutions to cover the entire globe, an optical scanner would scan a strip of surface a few kilometres wide and gradually enable a detailed surface map to be built up at the Earth-end of the radio link. Thus long before man is able to build an astronomical observatory in an Earth satellite vehicle his instruments will be capable of obtaining high-definition pictures of planetary surfaces.

Similarly, by allowing missiles to travel to destruction in planetary atmospheres and telemeter data to Earth as they do so, it will be possible to assemble data concerning these atmospheres without assuming manned interplanetary expeditions. Accordingly while we are not likely to see manned space voyages for some considerable time yet due to the engineering and economic problems involved, probe rockets should prove valuable tools in astronomical and astrophysical research during the coming fifty years. Moreover, such probes will act as pilot experiments for manned vehicles which will undoubtedly be developed during the next century.

FIG. 8.13—Imaginary view of an Earth-satellite vehicle acting as a solar observatory. A plastic bag solar mirror is collecting solar radiation for the power supplies and spectroscopic synoptic measurements. An aerial system is homed on the Earth.

Facing p. 162

REFERENCES

[1] GRIMMINGER, G., *Jnl. Applied Physics*, **19**, 947, 1948
[2] OVENDEN, M. W., *Jnl. Brit. Interpl. Soc.*, **6**, 157, 1947, **10**, 275, 1951
[3] GOLD, T., *Proc. Gassiot Comm.*, Oxford, 1953
[4] HOHMANN, W., *Die Erreichbarkeit der Himmelskörper*, Ch. IV, R. Oldenbourg, 1925
[5] BURGESS, E., *Aeronautics*, **27**, 26, 1952
[6] BURGESS, E., CROSS, C. A., *Jnl. Brit. Interpl. Soc.*, **12**, 72, 1953
[7] CLARKE, A. C., *Jnl. Brit. Interpl. Soc.*, **7**, 49, 1948
[8] BURGESS, E., CROSS., C. A., loc. cit., 6

General.

The Establishment and Use of Artificial Satellites, E. BURGESS, *Aeronautics*, **21**, 70, 1949
The Artificial Satellite, E. BURGESS, *The Engineer*, **193**, 456, 1951
The Artificial Satellite, *Proc. 2nd Internat. Congress on Astronautics*, Ed. L. J. CARTER, British Interplanetary Society, 1951

BIBLIOGRAPHY

The following books cover in a more specialized manner the various matters discussed in the text of this book, and are suggested for further study.

The Upper Atmosphere, S. K. Mitra, Royal Asiatic Society for Bengal, Calcutta, 1948, revised edition 1952.

Rocket Research in the Upper Atmosphere, Ed. H. S. W. Massey, Pergamon Press, 1954, the complete papers presented at the Gassiot Committee Conference, Oxford, 1953.

Physics and Medicine of the Upper Atmosphere; a Study of the Aeropause, Ed. C. S. White, University of Illinois Press, 1952.

High-Altitude Rocket Research, H. E. Newell, Academic Press, U.S.A., 1954.

Geomagnetism, S. Chapman, J. Bartels, Oxford Clarendon Press, 1940 (2 vols.).

Cosmical Electro-Dynamics, H. Alfven, Oxford Clarendon Press, 1950.

Oscillations of the Earth's Atmosphere, M. V. Wilkes, Cambridge University Press, 1949.

Radio Astronomy, B. Lovell, J. A. Clegg, Chapman & Hall, 1952.

The Aurorae, L. Harang, Chapman & Hall, 1951.

The Atmospheres of the Planets, Ed. G. P. Kuiper, Cambridge University Press, 1949.

Analysis of Temperature, Pressure and Density of the Atmosphere Extending to Extreme Altitudes, G. Grimminger, Rand Corporation, 1948.

Rocket Propulsion Elements, G. P. Sutton, Wiley, U.S.A., 1949.

Rocket Propulsion, E. Burgess, Chapman & Hall, 1952, revised edition, 1954.

Ballistics of the Future, J. M. J. Kooy, J. W. H. Uytenbogaart, H. Stam, Holland, 1946.

Development of the Guided Missile, K. W. Gatland, Iliffe, 1952, revised edition, 1954.

INDEX